LESS THAN HUMAN

by
Lorraine Starke

DORRANCE PUBLISHING CO, INC.
PITTSBURGH, PENNSYLVANIA 15222

DEDICATION

This book is dedicated to all of the families and staff who, in their relentless struggles to maintain care and treatment for the mentally ill in this country, have faced legal barriers that have caused frustrations, fears, tears and anxieties.

I hope their unending endeavors will be rewarded by more tolerance and human interest and a public demand for governmental responsibilities toward these afflicted individuals.

It is hoped, through all of their efforts, a better and more substantial mental health system will surface to protect patients and society alike.

This battle is not over–It has just begun! There should not be homeless mental patients, and there should not be mental patients in our jails!

Public awareness and concern is a vital element to arouse governmental officials.

God will bless those who involve themselves for the good of mankind!

THE AUTHOR

The author has forty years of experience as a registered nurse and has been practicing psychiatric nursing for the past twenty years. Early references in this novel came from personal experiences as to the treatment found in state mental institutions and the overcrowded conditions which existed in the early history of these institutions.

Affiliation as a student nurse in 1950 opened the eyes of a young, impressionable girl to the fact that a world other than the one she had known existed.

Recognizing mental illness as an illness was then, even more than today, very difficult for some.

A return to psychiatric nursing in 1970 after a twenty year absence lead to the discovery that many changes had taken place. Psychotropic medications, which could control behavior patterns of many schizophrenics, were then in existence and deinstitutionalization had been set into motion in many states.

Working with the mentally ill has broadened her tolerance toward others. Getting to know each patient as a separate person and getting responses from them is quite rewarding.

The chronically mentally ill are being evicted from safe environmental surroundings when alternative programs are not in place to continue the care and treatment of these individuals. Emotions aroused by these conditions are those of anger and contempt for the system, and these feelings permeate the families and patients conjoined in similar conditions from one state to another.

Reverie about the past–and a hope for the future–arising from public concern for the mentally handicapped may help to create a better mental health system. The facilitation of public outcry on this subject is the purpose of this book.

PREFACE

The information given in this book is written in simple terminology so as not to complicate the issue of what mental illness entails. It should display the truth about political maneuvering, by influential special interest groups, to influence politicians, whose monetary concerns displace concerns for human rights for the unfortunates of society. The old idea of "Money talks and bullsh-t walks" appears to be the reason behind the entire deinstitutionalization plot in this country—only to find that it does not work. It is hoped that this information will arouse the consciousness of society and perhaps produce better insight and concern toward the care and treatment of the mentally ill. The general apathy of society towards these afflicted individuals has made it possible for government officials to monopolize the concept of "community placements" without encountering an antagonistic element which might have demanded an explanation of policies and procedures. An ignorant public lies dormant regarding the affairs which personally do not affect them.

The concept of deinstitutionalization is excellent in theory, providing that treatments for the mentally ill have a definite beneficial prognosis for all. As in all illnesses, what works for some does not work for all. The individual cases of mental disorders and schizophrenic patients whose histories are mentioned here are true; however, actual names have been exchanged for fictitious ones. You may gain a better understanding of mental illness and, especially, of the hard-core or "terminally ill." You may determine for yourself whether all patients are suitable for community placement or if there is a real need for an institution to provide care, protection and treatment.

All mentally ill patients risk a relapse when cessation of medication occurs. The hospital is a revolving door for the recidivists, or long-termers, who are unable to function for any extended period of time within the less routinized parameters of society. The communities simply do not believe they can be discharged anymore. It has already been proven that these individuals cannot function in the community without compliance to the medication routines. Schizophrenia is not curable, only controlled.

Schizophrenia is defined in the dictionary as a mental disorder involving splitting of the personality. Period! This is all that anyone wants to know. To live with a schizophrenic means more than what just a simple definition implies. It is a stressful and sometimes ferarful situation at home, disruptive to the family unit and threatening to both the family and the individual afflicted with a completely altered personality.

Schizophrenia is the major clinical and theoretical problem confronting psychiatry today. The behavioral aspects of this disorder that attract the most attention are the physiological manifestations, which are accepted; but few are willing to track down the organic findings. There is no universal, rational method of treatment. Schizophrenia not only involves the suffering patients and their families but the community as well. Many schizophrenic individuals are unhospitalized and continue their daily bizarre mannerisms without benefit of diagnosis. The old saying "They're not all in there!" can be seen as correct. In every neighborhood, you can usually hear someone say "He's crazy" about one of its inhabitants.

Psychiatrists are still, for the most part, making guesses at the etiological riddle. They do not wait for the appearance of delusions, bizarre regressive behaviors or hallucinations to make their diagnosis of schizophrenia. These are usually the secondary group of symptoms preceded by the primary symptoms of withdrawal, low self-esteem, thought disorder and a distorted sense of reality.

A family will have a child who behaves perfectly normally in every respect until he or she reaches the late teens or early twenties when the onset of schizophrenic traits begins. Changes occur in normal behavior: displaying withdrawal; self-isolation; sometimes threatening, abusive or destructive behavior; irritablility; temper tantrums; or inability to be reasoned with. This can be very frustrating to the family until the behavior is diagnosed as an illness. At this earlier stage, before it is identified as a mental disorder, they feel guilt, shame and disgrace and wish not to reveal their family problem.

As previously stated, the onset of symptoms could start in the late teens or early twenties, perhaps brought on by adolescent turmoil, recently acquired physical maturity, vocational expectations, disruption of ego functioning and extreme fatigue. We do not know if schizophrenia is an organic or a behavioral maladjustment brought on by adverse events in environmental surroundings. An early interpersonal traumatic experience can be one of the precipitating factors effecting later years.

Schizophrenia can be helped by group therapy and by working through relationships between both doctors and patients and patients and patients. Individuals with an understanding of their own behaviors can overcome difficulties in some instances, with the support of group members. For example: a fifty-nine-year-old woman was hearing voices, and they were listening to everything she said. No matter where she would go, they could hear her. She attended a therapy group as suggested by her physician. After listening to the various stories of the others in the group, she stated, "I don't have any problems!" This was her first experience with any disturbance in her usual stature. She went home and followed her medication routine–which was slowly dimin-ished–and now, at the age of eighty-one, she is functioning quite well and is in good contact with reality. Becoming a member of the therapy group awakened her sense of reality and, recognizing her differences, she helped herself become well. As in all cases of physical or mental awareness, recovery can occur if the mental outlook is positive. Slow diminishment of disturbed behaviors may have been a reflection of increasing adjustments.

Today science is researching the DNA factor, which may prove that the lack of or the addition of a chromozome could be the precipitating factor in predisposition to schizophrenia. Until this can be corrected in the early stage of life through science, research and experimentation, society must realize that mental illness is not the fault of the individual.

We are seeing more schizophrenic states due to abuse of drugs and alcohol and the concurrent destruction of brain cells caused by their usage. Many times environment and stress will precipitate depression, irritablility and mental illness. Not everyone can handle stressful situations for a prolonged period of time. Those who cannot will thus climb inside themselves to escape from reality. There are many forms and patterns of mental illness. The public will respond to and address muscular dystrophy, heart disease, cancer research, the handicapped, senior citizens, human rights, abortion and AIDS, etc., but they will not address this issue. You have never seen a telethon to aid research for the mentally ill. It is not only this country: the entire world will not address the issue of the mentally ill. It's about time the public is educated and made aware that mental illness is just that–an illness–and should be treated as such.

Let us hope that one day families will come forth and not be intimidated or ashamed when mental illness strikes one of their members. Let us hope that an educated public will become more involved–and care enough–to pursue state and federal concerns and involvement in the care and treatment of its mentally ill citizens.

The public remains unsympathetic, non-caring and ignorant about mental disorders. Families usually hide their identities when a member is identified as mentally ill lest the community harass and ridicule the existence of the individual. Today there are medications which can be given, and many of these patients can function in the community and remain in control.

The mentally ill are not "less than human."

"Human Beings": What are we? A man's bodily nature. What a product of nature with origins, heredities and environment, with fundamental physical and chemical make-up. It is the greatest of all puzzles.

What is a human mind? This is also a mystery. We are in a universe of reality. Are we more mental than physical, and how does this affect how we manage our lives? The question is: What are we and what can we do about situations in which we exist today? Everything enters our mind through our senses: sight, hearing, smell, taste, touch, etc. Reality is experienced by these senses. Our minds are similar to modern computers, storing all events experienced by our senses and recalling them.

The following words will be used often throughout this book, and a generalized meaning of such words will make reading easier. These are the names and the descriptions of various symptoms displayed in mental disorders:

1) *Disorientation–* Unable to recognize time, place, person; a disturbance in attitudes and perceptions.
2) *Attention Span–* Impaired; cannot focus on one activity; easily distracted.
3) *Appropriate–* A normal condition, behavior or attire.
4) *Inappropriate–* Disharmony of speech, thought and/or emotional feelings.
5) *Apathy–* Detached from, or having no interest in, surroundings or persons.
6) *Anxiety–* Apprehensive, unfocused fear.
7) *Irritability–* Easily annoyed; low frustration level.
8) *Aggression–* Forceful action with a counterpart of anger, hostility and rage.
9) *Stupor–* A lack of reaction and awareness of surroundings.
10) *Restless–* Confusion and fear.
11) *Somnolence–* Abnormal drowziness.
12) *Insomnia–* Inability to sleep.
13) *Hypoinsomnia–* Exact opposite of the above, excessive sleeping. Common in the state of depression.
14) *Overactive, or Hyperactive–* Restless, aggressive or destructive activity.
15) *Hypo-Activity–* A visible slowing of thought, speech and movements.
16) *Mutism–* Voiceless; in psychiatry, often not a physical abnormality, but a choice.
17) *Pre-Occupation–* Only responds to stimuli (hearing voices) or hallucinations.
18) *Incoherent–* Muffled, garbled speech; cannot understand thoughts or words.
19) *Hallucination–* Can be auditory, visual or tactile: seeing things that aren't there; a false perception of sight, people, images or sensory touch or smell. Hearing voices, noises, etc. Example: "Bugs are crawling all over me!" "Did you hear them tell me to jump?"
20) *Delusions–* A false, absurd belief, such as, "I'm John Wayne," "The TV is watching me," or "I'm Jesus Christ" etc.
21) *Agitation–* Restlessness; can contribute to a state of anxiety.
22) *Depression–* A feeling of sadness, self-pity and, sometimes, low self-esteem.
23) *Mood Swings–* As seen in manic depressives, euphoria to depression and anxiety.

24) *Flat Affect*– Expressionless, monotonous voice and blank facial expression.
25) *Flight of Ideas*– Conversations usually rapid, with constant shifting from one subject to another. No consistency when conversing.

Benjamin Rush (1745-1813)– Wrote the first general book on psychiatry in America. He was known as the father of American Psychiatry, and was the most famous physician of his time. He was also a signer of the Declaration of Independence.

Joseph Adams (1756-1818)– Englishman who wrote the first book on hereditary properties of diseases; he argued that mental illness is not a disease but was inherited. His idea was that a person was susceptible to disease; therefore, prevention and cure of mental illness was possible.

Sigmund Freud (1856-1937)– Was the first to discover how to use a person's unconscious state in treating psychiatric patients; he was also the founder of psychoanalysis.

Dorothea Dix (1803-1887)– She is known as the most famous reformer of institutions for the mentally ill. She was not a nurse but a school teacher in the state of Massachusetts. She was shocked and appalled at the living conditions of the mentally ill, finding that a large number of them were accumulated in the jails or poor houses of her state. Dix was the first to have the mentally ill released from the jails by declaring that they were ill, not criminals. She lead the founding of asylums for the mentally ill and demanded that they be treated. She traveled around the country influencing twenty other states to build asylums, release the mentally ill from the jail and poor houses and treat them for their illness.

The United States Government appointed her Superintendent of Army Nurses. She was very strict and chose plain and sober women between the ages of thirty-five and fifty. These women would become an asset to the Army, and she insisted that their appearance be neat and orderly.

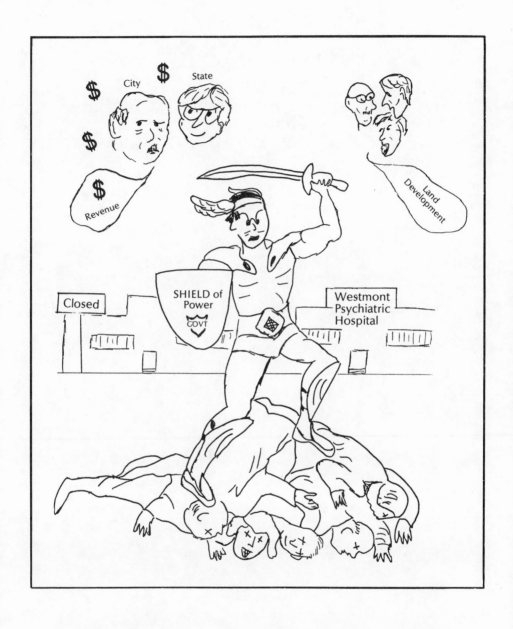

Expelled from Hospitalization
What will Happen to them now?

CHAPTER ONE

Mental disorders have been present since the beginning of man. It was not recognized as an illness but rather, possession by a demonic personality, perhaps the devil, or some sort of witchcraft. These people were misunderstood, feared and were the pinnacle of laughter because of their portrayal of unusual, erratic and bizarre behaviors. Some called this madness inspired by the gods. Their manifestations of various psychological mental disorders were confusing to the "normal" society.

Families of the mentally ill would experience persecution and exclusion from society. Because of ignorance, shame and guilt, the afflicted would be hidden away from society, and sometimes chained in attics or basements, so that families could avoid confrontation from their neighbors.

Some of the mentally ill were severely beaten, because many believed that demons were inside of their bodies. Some mentally ill people were burned at the stake; it was feared that they were witches. Many times when violent behaviors would erupt, they were chained and beaten, as if this would make them slide into docile, submissive behavior. Others were never approached while chained; people were afraid of being harmed.

The mentally ill could be chained or hidden for years and other family members or neighbors would never know of their existence. It is a known fact that when the Indians captured a "white man," and if he acted "crazy," they would refuse to kill him, fearing that the evil spirits would escape and harm them or perhaps even enter their bodies.

When recognition of the abnormalities of psychosocial behaviors surfaced, the mentally ill were institutionalized or warehoused strictly for the protection of communities, but knowledge of treatment was nil. They then became pawns in the field of experimentation.

All forms of unknown, different diagnoses of mental disorders, and the different categories in which they fall, were housed together. There was no protection from peers who would display hostile, threatening, destructive and abusive behaviors. Historical abuse of patients on patients, as well as staff on patients, was rampant. The "wild ones" would be strapped down to a bed or chair and ignored until meal time. There has also been evidence of patients being chained to walls and badly beaten when out of control. On several occasions in different institutions, patients were burned to death when fires broke out because they were chained to the walls, were not released and were abandoned by the staff.

These unfortunates were not visible to the public, and there were thus no feelings of concern for their welfare. Animals were treated better than these human beings afflicted with an illness.

It has only been within the last two hundred years that mental disorders were considered within the province of medicine. Psychiatry emphasizes the humane and compassionate aspects of medicines that deal with mental disorders and diseases, behavioral and psychological manifestations.

Psychiatry was the last specialty incorporated into medicine. There were no medications available to control behaviors, and the experimentation began.

Williamsburg, Virginia–known then as the Eastern State Hospital–opened October 12, 1773, twenty-two years before the Pennsylvania Hospital of Philadelphia admitted insane patients into their hospital. Williamsburg was the first hospital built in the colonies specifically devoted to mental illness and was operated under the direction of the state.

The first mental hospital built in the North was in Worchester, Massachusetts in 1833.

When violent patients were admitted, they were placed into seclusion and dosed with narcotics; if that didn't work, they were given showers or prolonged baths. And if these procedures proved ineffective, patients were restrained with leather wrist bands or

Forlorn – Forgotten
Chained in the Attic

mittens.

Opium was the best narcotic, as it was believed that it removed symptoms of insanity. It also produced withdrawal of delusions from the mind and cured insomnia.

Warm baths were given to subdue nervous irritability and excitement. The baths would last one to two hours, while cold water was "gently" sprinkled on the head.

Kindness was stressed, as it was believed to be effective in producing confidence while helping to reduce feelings of isolation.

Hospitalization did not mean total removal from the "sane" world and sane people, but was a substitute with healthier influences than some morbid associations at home, and it also provided protection.

Patients were kept together in homogeneous groups, becoming accustomed to each other and sharing other patients' point of views, which would help each patient out of their reveries. Today, this idea may be considered the same as group therapy.

Slaves cared for the mental patients in Eastern State Hospital, but were used mostly for preparing the meals, the cleaning tasks and the wash. They continued to work there until the Civil War.

Patients crowded together produced escalations of behaviors, and when farming and occupational therapies were introduced, it proved to be beneficial as patients that were kept busy relaxed more and usually displayed subdued irritability. This also produced less incidents among patients.

Dorothea Dix came to Williamsburg often when she toured mental hospitals throughout the country. She would bring books, pictures and materials for quilts. Occupational therapy, growing vegetables, dairy farming, raising chickens, etc., had not only produced some improvement in patients but was also a financial aid.

Mental patients differ from "normal" society by their deviant behavior and thought with reference to a person's total personality. Predisposing causes such as physical or social conditions can be difficult or impossible to control.

When psychotherapy failed to control behaviors, there would be a frontal lobotomy to subdue the violent actions of the patients. Belief of success was widespread–the patient was more manageable–but they became vegetables, and their memories would often be erased. There were times when this procedure was somewhat successful but, on the whole , it was really inhumane.

4

Today this is not evident in their treatment. One example which you may recognize is the Hollywood film "One Flew Over the Cuckoo's Nest". The film was made to amuse the public and their reaction was anticipated: Everyone wanted to see the film. The public was not sympathetic nor did they gain insight into the miseries of the patients' existence.

As seen in the film, Electric Shock Therapy–EST–was introduced and widely used on a regular basis. It had some degree of success in subduing violent behavior, but it would also erase some memory in a few of the patients. It is still used today in a more sophisticated procedure and often only as a last resort when there is no response to medication. It has been a useful tool in some cases of severe depression.

Mental institutions were built in many states around the country. They were not referred to as "mental hospitals," but "Insane Asylums" or "Asylums for the Criminally Insane."

Westmont was also built in that era–about eighty years ago–and specifically housed poor mental patients. Various institutions which were privately built were for the privileged people who would be able to pay for their internments. If the monies were depleted and continued care was required, patients were transferred to the state facilities. These places then became a dumping ground for families to rid themselves of older relatives who became a nuisance. Commitment to these facilities was rather easy in this time and soon these institutions were doing nothing more than warehousing people.

Even in that era, people could become committed with the use of political interest. And if the right politician or judge could be bribed, the patient–at the request of his or her family–could easily become a patient in the state institutions.

Derelicts from city jails or bums off the streets could be picked up by the police and transferred to an institution. There is no doubt that many of the people interned were just unfortunates or seen as a nuisance to society. The city's general hospital made regular weekly transfers to the state institution when their wards became crowded, especially if there were cases with no family involvement. Once admitted there, it was almost impossible to hope for a discharge. These people remained in the facility for many years.

Over the centuries, the lunar influence on the earth has been widely recognized. During the full moon, the ocean tides seem to be effected, rising higher than normal; in the presence of storms, it can cause a threat to the shorelines and is often blamed for flooding conditions. The full moon is also blamed for precipitating labor contractions and increased birth rates in terminal pregnancy cases. Hospital records can collaborate these facts by the increase in birth records during this period.

The mentally ill have been known to escalate their erratic, psychotic behaviors during the full moon period. The term "lunacy" was associated with mental illness, and the mentally ill would be referred to as "lunatics." But, on the other hand, society can suffer from the "blues," experience emotional swings or display a mild state of depression.

Studies have been made concerning the effect of atmospheric pressures and the weather elements on the psyche. A comparison of dreary weather with that of direct sunlight and pleasant weather conditions shows how each can effect behaviors or agitated states. It was shown that in the Northern States more episodes of agitation occur than in the warmer and sunnier Southern States.

There have been light studies connected to unstable individuals with positive results, showing diminishing states of agitation and a calmer, more-in-control behavior. Some individuals wore rose-tinted glasses that seem to have subsided irritable behaviors. In others yellow-tinted glasses seem to have effected them in a more positive manner. As individuals are different, different methods and different colors worked well on one person more than another. These stories are not concrete nor are they written in stone, but they open other avenues in the treatment of mental illness.

Mental illness covers a very wide path. There is no one set of symptoms for all categories. There is no one set of behavioral patterns to fit all of those afflicted. Mental disorders could be described as "disorders of the mind," encompassing numerous bizarre, erratic, unusual and different forms of behavior.

Just as varied as the interpretation of mental disorders is the different treatments each individual may receive. Why are there so many types of medications, and why do some work for one individual and not the other?

Schizophrenia has many faces and titles: catatonic (stupor), paranoid (chronic undifferentiated type), affective type, borderline, atypical, etc. Mental illness is almost as different as the individuals effected! It may be seen in one small episode, the display of some

Self Protection

disturbance and easily abated; it may vary in intensity from mild to severe and become persistent at frequent intervals.

Community approaches, which are full of promises, have not lived up to expectations. On one hand the large population of state mental hospitals has been greatly reduced, but, at the same time, communities are not always prepared to handle them.

Recently the "norms" have changed and, with them, thoughts are changing to what is considered devious; for example, persistent masturbation was once considered devious. But now unusual life styles have gained acceptance for those who wish to engage in them. In 1973-74, when the American Psychiatric Association held their conference, it was decided to drop homosexuality from its diagnostic manual of mental illnesses. This was not a unanimous decision but was still considered a landmark change in view point. This illustrates that there is no single unambiguous definition to distinguish the mentally healthy from the mentally ill.

Mental illness is a term which should only be applied when all tests of physical anomalies are exhausted. Bizarre behaviors, as well as depressive states, can be caused by other conditions and may not necessarily be true mental illness, but a side effect of a physical condition, impairment of brain tissue function caused by infections, intoxications or trauma, poor nutrition, disturbance of metabolism, hypoglycemia, side effects from medications, etc.

Before determining a "true schizophrenic," a physical work-up and assessment of the physical condition is important. A true schizophrenic may have excellent general health, and yet a hidden cause or chemical imbalance has not yet been established. It remains as much of a mystery today as it was in the Dark Ages.

At one time it was believed that if no organic lesion was present then it was not a disease, and the patient was not considered "sick." They were more or less thought of as criminal or immoral. "Madness" was the term, and madhouses were established in the thirteenth century to incarcerate the insane. And yet there was no treatment–none was known.

The term "bedlam" was probably derived in London which had one of the earliest institutions, Bethlehem Hospital. The standard equipment included chains, locks and keys and stocks. People visited Bethlehem to watch the bizarre behaviors of its inmates–this was one of "the sights" in London! The term "bedlam" is associated with riots, confusion and disturbances.

It had been rumored for years that Westmont would close.

No one would believe this because we were the only facility available for the largest city in Eastern Pennsylvania. In the fifties and early sixties it housed 7,000 patients. At that time–before the introduction of Thorazine and other psychotropic medications which could stabilize some behavioral problems and allow schizophrenic patients to function in the communities–you could call it "warehousing." This was a great breakthrough in mental health, helping patients to become more appropriate for existence in the community. The great push began. In coordination with the exodus, committees were formed to survey environment, staffing and patient care in an institution setting. Monitoring by these groups ensured that treatment and care would be upgraded, and the quality of care did greatly improve.

New policies and procedures were introduced, and the hospital would have to conform or loss of funding would result. These continuous observations by various teams were beneficial to patients and staff alike. Peonage was halted and recreational programs were instituted. "Patient's Rights" were also mandated as a protection. The days of leather restraints at the will of the staff, tepid tub baths for hours, crowded wards, peonage, nudity, etc. were passe. Floor space per patient was mandated, wards were painted in bright colors, curtains were placed on windows, hanging plants and an overall new awareness of the importance of environment, made a tremendous difference. With more monies, these things could be accomplished.

As the years passed, patients continued to be discharged; and in the late eighties, the hospital population had decreased to approximately five hundred patients. The patients remaining were those in which treatment, therapy and medications were ineffective. These patients were considered to be the hard-core mentally ill, many of whom had long histories and prolonged hospitalizations or were a threat to others or themselves; others were too confused, disoriented, lacked survival skills and needed a safe, protective and structured environment.

One late summer night in 1987, a group from the State Capital swooped down and fired the top administrators of Westmont. Most of the hospital's staff was informed via the early morning radio broadcasts. When arriving at the work site everyone asked, "Is it true?" The reason given was incompetence and irresponsibility in the performance of the administration. This was the first axe to fall; the wheels had been set in motion. This was the first shady step in the state's plans to close Westmont. This was the first inkling of awareness to the possibility of closure. Today every person who was toppled from their post was given other, similar positions within the state system.

The governor had been elected the previous year after struggling for twenty years before successfully winning an election. It is widely believed that a deal was made between the mayor of this large city, the only newspaper in town, The Quest and the governor. The ground on which the hospital stands is a valuable piece of real estate with vast acreage. This was a Garden of Eden for these mental patients. They had grounds and could wander, lie in the grass or just enjoy the outdoors. When weather permitted family and friends would picnic when visiting. This was a perfect non-confining atmosphere for appropriate patients to enjoy. Activity groups would have cook-outs and games; yearly picnics were held, which provided food, games, prizes and music for dancing. At these picnics you could see patients respond to music and dance. These were patients who would sit all day withdrawn and isolated. How therapeutic these activities were!

The grounds extended enough to gain the attention and interest of land developers who began to bargain for control of it. The revenue which could be collected would benefit the city and the state. Yes! These grounds were too valuable for the "mental patients." Again no consideration was given to the people who would be uprooted and placed who-knows-where. The welfare of the patients and their families were expendable. These patients were considered "less than human," as they could not defend themselves against the bureaucrats. These patients were not a voting block to contend with; and the grounds on which the hospital stood were not a tax base.

The next axe to fall was the appointment of a "Blue Ribbon Committee" by the Secretary of Welfare, who was also recently appointed by the governor to oversee the overall management of the hospital. Mr. Whitman would act as the governor's puppet to accomplish the closing procedure. A conference was arranged between Mr. Whitman and the entire staff of the hospital. No one will forget his first words: "We are not here to close Westmont." The events that lead up to his next bold statement would need some ground work. The news media and the city's only newspaper, The Quest, would be the primary source used to brainwash the naive public.

10

Media Bashing
Hospital and Staff

The media was invited to the hospital by the administration and was personally escorted from building to building, including entrance to the wards. The patients were again used and their right to privacy violated. There were cameras and questions, especially when they saw a patient in four-point restraints. The media stated that because he was a seizure patient, he was being abused. It had not been reported that he had frequently attacked staff and peers alike. It was not reported that staff members had been injured and were often on disability leave due to injuries from this patient. It was not reported that he had often attacked his father when he was visiting with him. Due to the publicity he received and the sympathy of the public to this abuse, the family obtained a lawyer, and sued the state and won an enormous settlement of which the lawyer gained quite a percentage. The stage was now set in the public's eye: There was terrible abuse at the hospital!

Patients are not restrained for the convenience of staff, as portrayed on television and in the press–a physician's order is required. This is usually done for the safety and protection of self and others, and this is legal.

A segment of the news televised the old "Snake Pit" pictures and related the present abuse to the forties and early fifties, before psychotropic medications were introduced. They accused the staff of "historical abuse" and negligence; they also claimed irresponsibility, incompetence, laziness, physical and sexual abuse, the strapping down of patients like animals and almost any kind of abuse you could possibly imagine. Needless to say, this shocked everyone on staff at the institution as well as the public.
This portrayal depicted the staff in a negative way to the public. We did not recognize this as another step by the state to reach its goal of closure. It was clear that they would use every trick or means necessary to close us. Not only were the patients expendable, but the staff as well.

Under this disguise, the third axe fell before the Christmas holiday in 1987. Another meeting was held by the "Spartan" Mr. Whitman disclosing the termination plans for Westmont. Close Westmont! This had been the ultimate goal of the new governor and his henchmen. Mr. Whitman appointed his assassins to perform in any manner they wished as long as the job was done. Ethel Richter was selected since she had experience as a "hatchet man" in the state of Ohio. She in turn chose her puppet, Lois Booker. The ultimate power would be given to Mr. Whitman's deputy, Mary

Knight. It is difficult to believe that these people dealt in human services, as it seemed that they had no heart at all. What they would accomplish for the mentally ill was one step forward and three steps back.

Where the television left off, The Quest picked up the momentum; the two medias bombarded the public, relentless in their efforts to assist the existing administration, as a preface to gain the public's consensus and support for their "Bold Plan of Community Placement." Emphasis was placed on "historical abuse." Physicians were accused of lack of medical and psychiatric treatment and evaluation of patients. The job was well done. Staff members were ashamed to give this hospital as a reference when seeking a position elsewhere. If the topic arose in conversation, staff members would be asked, "Do you work in that place?"

There was no consideration given to the families. The State Mental Health System had been deteriorating, using lack of money as the basis of reasoning in the decision to close the hospital.

Long Term Care was the first building to close. Looking back six years, it had been a pilot program of the state to open a long term care facility. It would bring in more funds for the hospital from federal as well as state budgets, so there was economic reason. Evaluation of senior psychiatric residents began and appropriate, "better" patients would be admitted. All of Long Term Care's residents came from within the hospital and broke the first rule of the state itself of placing geropsychiatric patients as clients. The psychiatric diagnosis was deleted as their primary diagnosis and only medical terms were used. The commitment number was also dropped since, legally, they could not reside in Long Term Care if they had a commitment number.

This unit was a separate entity with its own administrator, social workers, therapy groups, an O.T., recreation and music staff and a different cost center than the rest of the hospital. The rules and regulations also differed. The "open door policy" meant that patients could come and go as they pleased. Let us remember that coming from within the general hospital, most of these psychiatric patients were elderly, confused, disoriented, and regressed. These patients were really chosen by staff members wanting to rid themselves of older chronic behavioral problems, seizure patients, diabetics, incontinent and total care patients. Each ward had their own medical doctor and would only consult a psychiatrist if needed. Doses of medications were greatly reduced and would not be effective in controlling some behaviors.

The patients received excellent care because the staff had known them, and all of their idiosyncrasies and were dedicated to their welfare. In outside facilities such as ours patients did not receive one-to-one care with a dedicated doctor at the realm twenty-four hours a day. Decubiti were almost non-existent due to the nursing care they received. There was no urine odor to greet you as in many other nursing homes; in fact these patients were "the children" of the staff and were watched over continuously. They were closely monitored at meal time to prevent choking due to the fact that many of them were edentulous patients. Wandering by these patients had to be monitored continuously, as some of them dug in the trash cans and would put trash in their mouths.

On several occasions, quick action by the staff prevented choking deaths. There was never enough clothing, and many times when clothing was scarce the aides would wash enough underwear and socks to provide daily wear. Strangely enough, when J.C.A.H. or Medicaid and Medicare would arrive on grounds to evaluate the care, clothing was delivered in abundance from the warehouse to ensure that patients were properly dressed for these surveys. The meals would also look more appetizing on these occasions. Medical supplies and medications presented no problems, as there was never a shortage and the pharmacists were very reliable and competent.

The staff became tuned quite quickly to the new rules and regulations of the nursing home, but they had never before worked so physically hard on such a consistent basis. There was lifting and pulling, bathing and dressing; but the only complaint voiced was that when a patient left the ward or building a staff member had to run and find him or her. This open door policy might have done in a regular nursing home, but this facility was only a pretense, as it actually housed geropsychiatric patients who were confused and disoriented.

The state chose to close the Long Term Care facility first and selected Ethel Richter and Lois Booker to handle the closure. They waited for the first opportunity to justify this decision, for any neglect or abuse which might gain attention. During the winter of 1988, their opportunity came. Two patients, Lennie Pierson and Cynthia Ricca, were found expired on the grounds, at different times, three weeks apart. Frozen to death! Perfect! The negative publicity started again, especially from the relentless newspaper.

14

No doubt that Lennie had become inebriated and could not find his way back to the building. He had a history of alcohol abuse and, due to the open door policy, found an opportunity to elope to a bar. He had a similar incident the previous summer when he was found during the early evening stoned in front of another building on the grounds and had to be assisted back to the nursing home with a wheelchair. His history of alcohol abuse was listed on his chart, and yet he was allowed to leave the building when he pleased. We could not infringe on his rights as a resident of the nursing home. Although the grounds were searched he was not found by security. And yet he was found on the grounds the next morning! Cynthia had been coming and going for thirty years or more. She was oriented and aware of what was going on. Why wasn't she found when the grounds were searched? Why was she also found the next day in daylight, in the snow, with no footprints around her? There was dried blood in the corner of her mouth and her underpants were missing. One of the staff members–who identified her body–stated that the snow appeared as if someone had brushed away all the footprints. It had not snowed overnight. Why was it stated that she had frozen to death in the snow? What was being covered up? The staff member who identified the body thought that foul play may have taken place. Cynthia had used obscene language with sexual im-plications quite frequently, and often said to other patients, "Here yar, fu— me." Just suppose she had gone to the corner store and behaved in this manner. There was always a gang of young men who hung around on that particular corner, and drugs were known to be a part of their scene. The open door policy and unlocked wards mandated by the state rules were the precipitating factor in causing these negligent and untimely deaths and yet the staff was blamed. The state was the real abuser!

Because of these two incidents, Ethel Richter and Lois Booker proceeded to fire the administrator and replace her with staff from Lerner's State Hospital. The new staff didn't want to be here and told everyone this almost on a daily basis. They were arrogant, changed schedules and procedures and remained aloof from the staff. They rarely said "Good Morning," or answered you if you said it. They made it clear: They certainly did not want to be here!

The next steps taken to close Westmont were carefully thought out–the State Department of Health was to be utilized. They would use their system of deficiencies to do it. They continued to appear every three to four weeks, picking at, harassing and acting

Separated for Life
Man and Wife

noncomplimentary when corrections were made. They only created new deficiencies, down to squeaky chairs and dull brass door hinges.

Crews worked around the clock scrubbing and cleaning, shining floors, changing curtains, painting walls and doors in brilliant colors and still they came and said, "We don't see any difference." No matter what was done or how the environment looked, Long Term Care would close! One of the Health Department personnel placed her finger into the mashed potatoes to see if they were cold. An aide told her, "I wouldn't eat that after your finger was in it!" They watched the aides feed the patients but never did they offer any help although there were so many to feed. All they did was criticize if the patient didn't want to be force-fed or refused what was offered. There were about fifteen patients that required spoon feeding and a staff of four aides. The aides would feed one, and then the next until all were fed. Maintaining their nutrition was quite a job; as you know, older people can be quite contrary.

As the census started to drop, the patients located in the back dormitories of a ward were uprooted to the front dormitory. This involved emptying lockers and bedside cabinets of personal items and placing clothing and personal items in their new location. With further depletion due to transfers out, the patients were again uprooted from their new dormitory to the other ward across the hall. The one ward, now empty, was locked. The process started all over again on the one remaining ward. As patients left the ward, the back dormitories were emptied and locked. This again meant changing lockers and bed areas for the patients. Remember, these patients were elderly, debilitated, a large number non-ambulatory and suffering from various medical problems.

This kind of uprooting only confirmed my feelings that in Booker and Richter's minds, these were only bodies to be condensed into one area. This moving process produced anxieties, feelings of insecurity and restlessness among patients and families. Lois Booker and Ethel Richter appeared often on the unit to monitor the discharging and transfers, portraying delight when the last patients would exit. By the end of June, 1988, the final patient who could be placed departed. The eleven patients who were not acceptable for placement were transferred back to the psychiatric units. Before admittance to these units, they had to appear in court for recommitment. At least now they would receive the psychiatric care they were denied while residing in the nursing home.

17

Booker and Richter had placed another feather in their cap by their compliance with the higher echelon mandates at the expense of the patients. Yes! These patients were treated as "less than human." Some patients were transferred to a distant place that was inaccessible to many relatives. For instance, Janet Clarke was eighty years old and her husband was about the same age. He traveled by public transportation every day to spend time with his wife. They only had each other; there were never any other visitors for her. She looked forward to seeing him every day. The staff would give him a tray at meal time and the two would talk together; occasionally she would kick him under the table and give him hell. At least they were together during the day. Now he would never see her again! She was wisked off by a state car to a remote mountain area where the state had another facility that took several hours to reach from Westmont. Many reports of patients expiring after transfers disturbed the staff. We felt sure that if they had remained here they would still be alive! The effect of uprooting elderly people and placing them in different environments with new personnel was devastating. Booker and Richter would know this if they were indeed qualified in the field of human services. It appeared as if they were moving cargo or freight instead of human beings. Their coldness and fake concerns for the welfare of these elderly patients was evident to all. These elderly patients, many with psychoses, were at the mercy of these state officials. Many placed persons were displaced. Families as well as the patients were upset. But their concerns for their relatives went unheeded.

After the dirty work was done, Booker and Richter were noticeably absent in the latter days of closure. As patients left daily it was like losing family. Concerns surfaced, "What would happen to them now?" Of course some patients didn't realize that they would not be returning to the nursing home. Others thought that it was just another day trip. These patients often went on bus trips to a nursery or an orchard. They often went out for ice cream treats or just a ride in the country.

The temporary, acting administration members from Lerner State Hospital were anxious to leave Westmont and return to their area. There was not even a thank you exhibited for the efforts of the long term staff who worked diligently packing and unpacking, moving and removing items and clothing during all of the patient shuffling.

Now the building was officially closed and the assignment

that Booker and Richter had been given was finally accomplished, with the help of the Department of Health and the news media. The bodies were gone and who cared? The staff from this unit was transferred to the psychiatric units. Thus ended the chapter of a nursing home in a state facility.

CHAPTER TWO

Westmont was no different from any other state institution. It had also come through the dark ages of psychiatry. They had their share of straight jackets, insulin shock and electric shock therapy. They gave cold water baths, wrist and ankle chains or restraints and seclusion rooms. There were massive doses of cathartics (laxatives) and emetics (vomiting drugs); extensive bloodletting and blistering; and other powerful drugs which had an impact on the body, inducing debilitation, shock, physical pain and terror in patients. These treatments had good intentions. It was not known–and still is not–whether mental illness has physical causes or is a result of brain disease. The wards were crowded and indigents, aged alcoholics, etc., were routinely admitted. Patients were placed in institutions mostly to protect society and thus were only given custodial care.

Westmont had a substantial staff-to-patient ratio. All necessary disciplines were in place and functioning quite well. The problem arose when the city funds became deficient and new sources of revenue were needed to stabilize the hospital's economy. Although the city administration had come into office with a surplus budget, its irresponsible spending, gifts to special interest groups and other maneuvers had bankrupted the city. The inflated contract agreements with unions–with no means to pay for them–resulted in tax hikes that still weren't sufficient. The administration now admitted that it had a deficit of $70 million.

Westmont happened to sit on a comfortable, large acreage of valuable real estate which could, if developed, bring in a sizable tax base. The governor was also interested in this piece of real estate and, together, conjoined a method of how it could be obtained. It is believed that deals were made with land developers to secure this property.

At the expense of protected mental patients, a "Bold Plan of Community Placement" was initiated. As stated previously, a Blue Ribbon Committee was organized to set the wheels of this bold plan in motion. With the sale of this huge property to land developers, and with businesses and cultural centers on these grounds, the state and the city could benefit financially through collected taxes. Let us not forget that the mentally ill neither pay taxes nor vote. What would they have to lose? Politicians, under the pretense of caring for these patients, made it seem more humane to place them in community settings. This was a great idea for appropriate, functioning patients who continued with their medication routines. It was agreed that the state and the city would share the needed funds to continue the proposed plan of placement.

One tool of advancement toward the goal of the closure of Westmont was several advocate groups consisting of former mental patients and liberals who could not fully understand the complexities of schizophrenics or the significance of discharging the hardcore, terminally ill mental patients into communities. Centers and half-way houses were put in place without forethought of the consequences. Unpredicted behavioral patterns surfaced causing chaos. Agreements were made with the police department and the newspaper, The Quest, not to publicize the events throughout the city resulting from these incidents. There was never mention of the suicides, rapes or assaults. Staff members who knew of these events wondered why there was no mention of them in the news media. The public should have been made aware of the dangers. The exact same thing happened in the dark ages when murders or assaults took place before institutionalizing. The newspapers never informed the public.

When Long Term Care closed, three large buildings were all that remained in operation on these beautiful grounds. Forty years ago the hospital housed 7,000 patients here with many crowded buildings in operation. Because of the discovery of psychotropic drugs, we had, through the years, been reduced to 500 patients. Patients enjoyed the blooming shrubbery and scattered pine trees, with squirrels and rabbits scamping about and the various birds flitting from tree to tree. This hospital was a perfect place with a non-confining campus for them to roam about. In the fall various brilliant colored leaves scattered about while the trees were preparing to lie dormant through the winter. Even when snow covered the ground, the trees were arrayed with glossy crystal decorations gleaming in the sunlight.

The admission unit was terminated in November 1988, denying access to recidivists and volatile patients. People in distress and other community residents could not be admitted here, in the largest city in the state and the only state facility for the mentally ill. It was difficult to accept by some; others were stunned by the decision, as they had relied on this facility to be in place if needed. Patients who were discharged and returned time and time again throughout the years were no longer supported. They were referred to their neighborhood community mental health center which was not aware of their medical histories.

At first these patients were sent by taxicabs to these facilities but it became an added expense to the state. Then they were escorted from the grounds by security guards and given only car fare. For several months, when the revolving door was finally stationary, patients appeared and reappeared attempting to get admitted as they had done before on many occasions.

When ex-patients became a nuisance by sitting in the lobbies or lying in the tunnels, a memo was issued to the effect that "squatters" should be reported to security and they would be removed. Keep in mind that we are talking about often confused, disoriented human beings afflicted with mental disorders. We are talking about recent discharges from this institution who were now being treated as intruders and less than human.

The news media again remained silent and the public was not made aware of these happenings. Patients began to be re-leased: many disappeared without follow-up teams, and some were adding to the city's homeless situation. It never would be discussed by the news media that a great percentage of these people were former mental patients. The patients who were not discharged by the psychiatrists were discharged A.M.A. (Against Medical Advice) by the city's court system. Judges were not qualified to render decisions without experience or knowledge of schizophrenic traits. The judicial system should not determine if the mentally ill could function in the community. They were not familiar with the bizarre, erratic behaviors which could occur at several month intervals instead of the suggested thirty to sixty day periods. The judges disregarded professional advice, leaving psychiatrists frustrated and demoralized. This has in the past resulted in catastrophies, causing the deaths of many innocent people nationwide and these incidents go on record to reveal the truth about these judgments.

Other professionals such as lawyers specialize in corporate law, civil suits, domestic relations, criminal law and real estate law. Should judges not be required to specialize in psychiatry, with a determinate affiliation in a psychiatric setting, to personally gain hands-on experience? This in turn would initiate responsible judgments, resulting in more beneficial outcomes for mentally ill patients and their families. The all-too-familiar political appointees now sit in judgment and are ignorant and irresponsible in their decision-making concerning mental patients. These people should be handled in a responsible, knowledgeable, dignified manner. Human rights also mean patient's rights. They have a right to receive consideration, treatment and care. They have a right to be protected from society and from self-harm. Decisions on discharges were based on a thirty-day record of subsided behaviors; it a patient had not acted out or portrayed any violent or assaultive behaviors, he or she was released.

John Keller is a good example of the harmful results of these judgments. John had been admitted six years previously with a history of violence, drug and alcohol abuse and robbery. He could remain calm and in control for several months. He cooperated with staff members, took his medications and attended community meetings. During these periods he was permitted on grounds, leaving the ward to enjoy the outdoors, returning for meals and medications. John loved to smoke cigarettes; if denied, this could lead to a period of hostility. He did not socialize with his peers and could care less about what they were doing. At times he could be observed responding to internal stimuli (hearing voices or seeing hallucinations). When demands were made by him and denied–or not immediately responded to–he would act out. During this period of hostility, he would knock down a peer who walked too close or punch the one nearest to him. If no one was near, he would then punch a wall. John would throw chairs or bang doors. He would become disruptive to the ward and would, on occasions, be secluded for a period of time until he regained control. He had a history of portraying this behavior at three or four months intervals.

On Wednesday, John would return to court and have a lawyer appointed to him. There had been no history during the past thirty days of assaultive, hostile or destructive behavior and he was therefore discharged through the courts. A few weeks had passed when it was reported that John had beaten his mother because she wouldn't provide him money on demand. He had also painted everything in her home with gloss enamel paint: curtains, sofa, floor and walls, etc. Mrs. Keller tried to have him committed in a metropolitan hospital but he was again released. John was infringing on the safety of his mother as well as destroying her property. Fear and anxiety were the conditions Mrs. Keller would have to endure. No further information was available as to the outcome or whereabouts of John.

Tyrone was a black male about 6'4" and weighing 280 pounds. He had a history of hospitalization since the age of seventeen. His was not a two-parent family and his mother did the best she could for her eight children. He received no attention at home and was average or below in school. At the age of fourteen, he turned to drugs and became truant from school. His work history is poor: the only job recorded was two months in a warehouse working as a laborer. He was arrested twice for burglary by the age of seventeen. He received psychiatric treatment in several facilities throughout the years before admission to Westmont. Occasionally he would become destructive and threatening on the ward. It always took five or six staff members to contain his behavior and place him into seclusion until stable. One week before his court hearing, another such incident occurred and he was placed into seclusion. Ironically, one week later, he was discharged through the court A.M.A.

Tyrone thought that by acting out he would gain the attention never given to him at home as a child. He was shocked at the decision, and when escorted from the ward for discharge, he had a blank, shocked facial expression and appeared very calm, as if in disbelief. The next day at lunch time, Tyrone was seen sitting in the lobby talking to other patients. This occurred for a period of two or three weeks, and then he was only sporadically seen. There would be no more meals, no more medications, no more attention. This was the only home Tyrone had known for twenty years. He was never seen again by the staff. It is unknown if he has a home or if he is living on the streets.

Many discharged patients were often seen living in the

tunnels of the hospital, only to scatter if approached. Staff members would feed them whenever extra trays were delivered. Some patients were seen walking in the woods behind the hospital: It was believed that they lived there somewhere. Ex-patients appeared off and on, with most looking disheveled, dirty and bearded. The staff was becoming outraged at the system and having to turn away ex-patients who appeared in need of care and medication. Families were also getting upset. The treatment of these human beings was an outrage to basic human rights. We could no longer be silent and allow this tragedy to occur.

The hospital instituted a system of evaluations which would be used to separate patients into categories. These evaluations would be performed by outsiders. These studies entail reviewing the patient's chart, past histories and interviewing the patient.

True evaluations and assessments should included input from the staff, patients and their families. When evaluating a patient, you must also take into consideration the presence of remissions. Twenty to thirty percent of schizophrenics admitted to a hospital, and treated only in a traditional, routine manner, can be expected to leave at the same stage of illness, displaying anxiety and sensory confusion. In remission the patient attempts to convince himself of the unreality of his delusions or hallucinations and will usually lack insight as to his or her illness.

An early detection tool to the traits of mental disorders is the testing of the thought disorder by various tests. Tests are clinically invaluable for psychiatric evaluations. One such test is word association; black–white; shoe–foot; salt–pepper; hair–comb. The patient's first response can usually signify their train of thought or indicate any confusion. Another known test used is known as the "ink blot test." You have seen these various tests performed in films as well as the responses which could detect an abnormality in the thinking process and provide estimates of its severity.

It is important for patients and doctors to communicate effectively. It is also important that to maintain emotional contact with the patient, doctors should strive to objectively and empathically understand him or her. When marked appearance of detachment and insensitive attitudes by the psychiatrist are present, the patient may become suspicious, hostile and abandon the relationship. The therapist is a representative of reality and should not only attempt to make contact with the patient but to maintain it by being accepted by the patient and gaining his trust.

Special evaluation groups from outside facilities were hired to view the patients and their charts for reassessments. When these outsiders, or intruders, were on the wards, other teams were sent to evaluate the care and treatment of these patients. Now the wards were continuously monitored by strangers with clipboards, hovering over staff members trying to perform their duties. These groups were also looking for the "historical abuse" and negligence portrayed by the press. This continued for a few months, and the situation became very stressful–and caused much anxiety–among the staff. It was difficult to work under these conditions and the staff started to call off sick. The patients, knowing that something was going on, were also upset. They wondered who these strange people were. Their feelings of insecurity were evident by their frequent behavior pattern escalations, which required the use of more P.R.N. medication. Families were also asking questions to which no one had answers.

Evaluations and assessments continued, and a handsome salary was paid to these groups per patient. Some evaluations were made by scanning the charts and interviewing the patients for ten or fifteen minutes. How could outsiders make a judgment about a patient's diagnosis and behavioral patterns so quickly and without input from the staff, social workers or families who knew the patients and their needs?

Charts were often pulled to the administration building and no now knew why. Were they just photocopying the information? It was reported that some information was being shredded in the machine, and that important facts were being deleted before evaluations were made. Without pertinent information a different evaluation could be made and the patient may very well appear appropriate for community living.

Patients began to be discharged either by the psychiatrists or the courts. Families would come to visit their relatives only to find that they had been transferred to half-way houses or other assessment areas. Some families engaged legal advice when the discharging process of the state's "Bold Plan of Placement" began. The lawyers consulted with the new, acting administration about their placement programs. There had been no follow-up of patients already released, and by January 140 patients could not be accounted for.

Two family support groups were formed with the sole purpose of relieving family tensions and assisting them to cope with the transition of releases. One group remained reserved while the other group was more outraged at the whole process and vehemently opposed the state's plan of closure. They felt they had the right to know when and to where their relatives would be transferred or released. Many families in the latter group could no longer cope with the patient's violent, destructive behavior in their own homes. Fear of self-harm, or fear of the patient, was a main factor. Some of the patients already released were known pedophiles, rapists or arsonists, manifested assaultive or destructive behaviors, or displayed threatening traits toward others. Still others were promiscuous and would do anything someone asked for a cigarette. We are talking about someone's daughter, son, wife, mother, brother, etc.

The wards in the buildings were buzzing with contempt for the state and their treatment of both families and patients. All disciplines were dissatisfied with the non-concern and cold application of their puppets–Booker, Richter and Knight–under Secretary of Welfare Whitman. His chief honchos, who were pulling all of the strings, set forth these asinine procedures for all to comply with.

They had placed the cart before the horse by discharging patients before Community Treatment Teams–"CTT"–were in place. The staff members selected for these teams were transferred from within the hospital–which the media had labeled incompetent, abusive and irresponsible–and suddenly became caring, concerned and responsive people.

Treatment teams were oriented for a period of weeks. Everyone seemed very enthusiastic about the program and were anxious to get started. Each person on the CTT team was given a list of patient's names whose cases they were to follow up. There were some patients out there who had difficulty adjusting to the community and unpublicized incidents were occurring. Families were sometimes not notified when patients were to return home and were assaulted or robbed by them. One patient unsuccessfully threw himself in front of trains on various occasions. One discharged person pushed a woman in front of a moving subway train in the city. This incident was mentioned on the news but they did not elaborate on the subject too much. A newspaper printed an article, appearing long after the incident, that the man had been a former patient of Westmont. One patient overdosed on drugs and was taken to a metropolitan hospital. One female patient was beaten so badly on the streets that she had to be admitted to a general hospital. Again, there was no publicity!

One patient tore up a supermarket, requiring eight police officers and mace to subdue him. One patient, who returned to the hospital on several occasions, committed rape on a female patient who was out on the grounds. He was removed from the property by state troopers and detained for a long period of time in a detention center. Statements were taken from eye witnesses who were told that they might be called to testify at a later trial. There was never a phone call or a hearing that the witnesses knew about. This patient now walks the streets. The gag was put on the media and the police. The word had been spread that there should be no publicity. This decision came from higher-ups in the state government. One AIDS patient who was discharged by the courts was seen working at a fast-food chain. He was later identified in the news media as the slayer of a police officer. The patient was also shot, by the officer, and died on the scene. The young police officer left behind two young children and a pregnant wife. This patient should never have been released into the community in the first place. This release left both a family man and the ex-patient–who was denied the care he needed to survive–dead. For all of the do-gooders who feel that institutions just lock up people this is one example that they do not truly understand the complexities of schizophrenic patients. They are not all the same, and do not fit into one category of schizophrenia with one set of symptoms for all. We are all individuals with different personalities and behaviors. As explained previously, "What works for one does not work for all!" The above incidents placed more burdens on an already taxed police department.

The city council and the mayor had been silent and would not address these incidents although it was evident that these patients were out of control. This was further conformation that the state, city and the only newspaper in town, The Quest, were working together to suppress the news. Usually the newspaper would pounce on a news item, but for the benefit of the city and state they remained silent. The Quest was assisting them by this lack of news to the public in order to not delay the Westmont closure.

Yes! The communities should have been fearful of these chronic, hard-core mental patients and would have had good reason to feel this way. These patients were a danger both to themselves and others.

CTT members only monitor patients for eight hours a day. What happens in the other sixteen hours? Who will clean, wash dishes, cook, do the laundry, monitor medications, smoking, personal hygiene and control agitated states? Will the police respond in time when this state of mind exists in the ex-patients? Should they care when there has been a "gag" placed on the arrests of these individuals? Will neighbors and their children be safe? Will communities be notified when residences in their neighborhoods are procured by the state for the placement of these mental patients? Where are the protection rights of the families and their communities when patients become out of control?

The staff knows their patients and knows what works! The mentally ill are entitled to be treated as human beings and we must recognize their rights. The staff was called many things by the press but they are actually the patients' real protectors! The state was the real abuser of patients and staff, and both were expendable when political deals made plans for the land. The state continues to snow-job the public and obliterate the truth by relating lies to the press and television media.

Close! Close! Keep it open! Keep it open! The state versus the families. Advocates for the mentally ill planned a march in which they would carry signs stating "Close Westmont!" The family support groups planned a counter-march the same day which resulted in the cancellation of the advocate's march. This would dilute the effectiveness of their purpose: To gain the attention of the public and sway their verdict towards closure. The administration did not want negative publicity. When the families arrived, they found security police in force! The families said that they only wanted to pray together to St. Dymphna, the patron saint of the mentally ill, for the patients. Other visitors were not permitted to visit that evening and were blocked off. Patients were kept on their wards inside the buildings. The families prayed and held a small meeting at the statue of the saint then left quietly.

Mr. Formbe lead the families in prayer at the statue of St. Dymphna and when one of the guards asked him what they were doing there, he said, "We're here to pray for the mentally ill and for the prevention of the closure of this hospital. Would you like to pray with us?" The guard walked away without answering him.

The next morning, when Mr. Formbe came to visit his son, he noticed that the statue was gone! The Blessed Mother and the fourteen foot cross, were also gone! He asked the administrators, "Why did you remove the statues?" Mr. Formbe was told that they were removed to prevent possible vandalism.

Mr. Formbe then asked the priest where the statue was and

29

Mental and Homeless

if he had placed it in the chapel located in the basement of one of the buildings. The Father stated that he had requested that it be placed there, but was told that it was probably already transported to another state institution.

St. Dymphna, patron saint of the mentally ill, had been removed! No doubt the officials didn't want the families to return to the grounds for any further prayer meetings.

This is how the state handles delicate situations–by removing them the same as they had done to Mr. Randall! Removal does not mean that people will forget, as the families remained active behind the scenes with the support of their lawyers.

As an old lady peeks out from behind a curtain–leering out occasionally to gather gossip–so did the administrators remain aloof. The proper thing for them to have done was meet with the families on this occasion, if only to quell their fears and reassure them in some way that their families would be protected. This could not be done, as the administrators themselves didn't know what the outcome of their "Bold Plan of Placement" and the transfers to other institutions would be.

The closing of the admission ward was a big mistake. The metropolitan hospitals could not handle the overflow of disturbed people requiring treatment.

It was a dull, cloudy Sunday morning when my eye happened to catch sight of a small, frail black woman advancing towards our building, which used to house admissions. She was disheveled and dirty, and the skirt she wore was stained with mud, food and who knows what else! There was a strong body odor, and it was evident that she had not bathed for a long time. She strolled into the lobby bathroom which only a former patient would have known the location of. She was not familiar to me but some other staff members recognized her as Hildra Walters, a former patient who had been discharged some time ago. I did not see her in the lobby and wondered where she had gone; she reappeared wearing clean clothing. The staff had taken her into the ward and showered her, gave her clean clothing and fed her from an extra ward tray at meal time. She now had cigarettes and a few dollars. This is the staff who was labeled as non-caring and irresponsible by the press.

They had washed and fed her and given her money and cigarettes. As related earlier in this book, she was considered a "squatter," and security guards arrived to escort her from the grounds.

"Why won't you let me stay here? Why are you trying to get rid of me? Please don't put me out in the streets again! I don't want to go back to the lice and bugs!" When security asked her how she came to be on the grounds, she replied, "The police dropped me off at the Boulevard and I walked in." Security insisted that she go outside and get into the state car. She angrily shook her shoulders, as if to say, "Don't touch me," hastily made a few gestures, scampered out of the building and down the steps and got in the back of the car. She would be dropped off at the edge of the grounds at the Boulevard where the police had put her in the beginning. This is proof that the city did not really want to be bothered, and that the policeman did not expect us to turn her out again. This is how we treat needy people in the land of plenty. Here is a woman begging to be cared for and treated who is simply turned away into the streets again. This is the great "Mental Health Program" dictated by the Government. This shows the lies portrayed on television by Mary Knight, who stated that we followed up our discharged patients with the CTT members. This proves that the placement programs were already failing.

Another incident of this sort happened in late July, 1989. It was 2:15AM on a clear Wednesday when a security guard entered the nursing office, accompanied by an elderly sixty-nine-year-old black woman. She was about four foot two and frail looking. The security guard had seen her walking on the grounds. She didn't look or act like a sixty-nine-year-old woman, and the beige pumps she wore did not appear to be old. Her hair was whitish-gray and curled to her head. There was a twinkle in her eyes, and barely a wrinkle was visible except for a few crow's feet in the corners of her eyes. The dress she wore was a plain, pinkish plaid and fell just below the knees. She was not aware that the neck facing was turned outward. No pocketbook or stockings were seen, but she tightly held a half-spent pack of cigarettes. The cigarette she carried in her right hand was burned down to the filter.

She was coherent enough although she had a little difficulty with some words because she was only wearing her upper dentures. She stated that her name was Alma Green.

"I only want a place to stay for the night," she said. "I didn't know you were closed."

"Where did you come from at this hour?" Mrs., Rounds, the night supervisor, asked.

"I got off the bus and walked here. I knew that Westmont was here."

"Do you have any money?"

"No. I got a card."

"Where is it?"

"I don't know. I can't find it now."

"Have you ever been a patient here?" Mrs. Rounds asked.

"No, I was in Germantown for high blood pressure. That's all. I want to go there and tell the doctor about AIDS and things,"

"What's the doctor's name?"

Mrs. Rounds was trying to gather information to help this woman but Alma's answers were too vague. She did state that her sister had died in 1988, and that she was living with a cousin but could not remember her name. With much prodding she came up with the name of Helen Sellers and the street that she lived on. She seemed to have no capacity to remember numbers, as she could not give the address or telephone number. Mrs. Rounds tried to find a Helen Sellers in the telephone directory but found that the name was not listed.

"We had a fight and I left," Alma said. "She lives on Willard Street, but I don't have the phone number or address."

Mrs. Rounds called the psychiatrist on duty to come and interview this woman, but Alma said that she didn't want to see the doctor right now. Dr. Rahju arrived, however, and could not get anymore information for the nurse than she already had.

"What year is this?: he asked her.

"Yes. It's 1989. Oh!–let me get out of here and get the bus!"

"Where will you go, do you know?"

"I'm going to Germantown, and thank you very much!" she yelled in an angry voice when she realized that she would not be allowed to stay and her time was being wasted. The security guard acquired a few tokens, escorted her off the grounds and waited for the bus to arrive before he would leave. When she boarded the bus safely, he returned to the hospital and said, in a very depressed tone, "It's a shame, isn't it?"

Westmont was not accepting admissions and here we were, turning out an elderly woman in the early hours of the morning, making her vulnerable to anyone out there who could victimize her.

What are we doing to humanity? We are turning our backs on it!

The mentally ill were unable to enter for treatment and, as a result, severely ill people, who would ordinarily be admitted, were clogging community hospital wards and were ending up on the streets. The precipitous closing of admissions flooded existing mental health systems with patients who had no place to go. Dr. Michael Vergare, president of the Philadelphia Psychiatric Society, stated that he had patients staying for long periods of time and couldn't transfer them to non-existent community services. Vergare stated that at one of the medical centers where he practiced, patients had stayed as long as 120 days in a ward designed for an average stay of 15 days. Jim Smith, the Director of Project Share, and an advocate of the patient self-help organization, had stated that the community hospitals couldn't carry the mentally ill any more, and had to proceed to find ways to rid themselves of them.

When Westmont stopped taking new patients, Smith knew of at least one hundred homeless people who had gone through crisis stages of their disease with symptoms that had gained them access to Westmont before. Mary Knight still stated that, "We make progress everyday," and denied that patients were virtually unserved, saying that "The city is serving them in existing programs!" Did she really believe this? Did she deliberately try to deceive the public and advocates when she knew full well that the facts were false?

Every so often an article about Westmont would be printed in The Quest stating that the closing of Westmont was a disservice and the chronically mentally ill require more intensive and complex psychiatric, social, vocational and rehabilitative service than do the mentally retarded. This indecent haste of closure before adequate substitute plans and facilities were in place constituted a profound and alarming failure in public policy and public accountability.

Another article stated, "The state decision to close is a profound failure to provide for the most helpless citizens of the state, the chronic, severely mentally ill. Eliminating the hospital does not eliminate the need!"

"The Snake Pit stigma is not easily erased. The lack of creative leadership from the state officials and the hospital administrators, and the lack of solid supervision and proper management of staff, has destroyed morale, so crucial to a mental hospital. Other forces are at work, such as the interest in the valuable land occupied by Westmont, and if the land were used in other ways it could be a real estate bonanza for the state and the city."

Deinstitutionalization! This is the cry heard throughout Commonwealths all over the country. Pennsvill discharged and placed all of their clients, but it took ten years to do it. Another mental retardation center took five years, after court mandates, when funds were promised to be put in place for community care. Now, without available funding, the retarded will be returning to institutional care. The two alternatives for families are reinstitutionalize or quit your job and care for them at home. For many the latter is an impossible choice.

Once services start to diminish, both the mentally retarded and the mentally ill sense a rejection by society. It seems as if we are riding a fiscal merry-go-round when allocating monies, always shifting priorities this area than that area. Now with the increasing AIDS problems, more monies are being distributed in those directions. The sick patients cannot be cared for anymore. The closing of institutions is just another disgrace that society has seen. The higher echelon of the states close facilities before other available resources are in place for these poorest of the poor.

California also had a budget axe. At Santa Monica West Mental Health Center, a psychiatric social worker, Robbyn Panitch, was murdered while on duty. She was killed by a homeless mentally ill man who was reportedly one of her patients. The staff became frustrated when the budget cuts caused shortages of services and staff, including security guards. This increased both the tension and danger for workers. California closed their buildings and sold the land where the institutions were. When their plan failed and the same problems arose, they decided to purchase more land to rebuild and place patients once more.

In New York, 1988, Clara Taylor, a psychiatric aide and mother of nine, was alone on the ward with approximately fifty mental patients when one attacked and killed her.

In Massachusetts deinstitutionalization increased the number of street people as well as crime. Many of these discharged patients ended up in the jails and were treated as criminals, not as mentally ill. They were placed alone in cells and given no medications. Here we go again, back into the dark ages. These were the conditions that Dorothea Dix had found before she started the reform of placing these people into asylums.

The state of Ohio tried the plan of community placement and had its share of incidents and crimes, as well as an increase of "street people."

Our government cuts the guts out of the mental health system and creates deep crises. If this is not "crazy," it is criminal. Understaffing invites danger and can cause injury and death. What the psychiatric aides provide is care, custody and control.

Budget plans are never enough to pay for the patients after the hospital closes. Already the state and the city are squabbling over their fair share of contributions toward the discharged and placed patients. Already they are saying that funds, as proposed in their budgets, are inadequate. Already the city has cut back funds for social programs. It is only now, with this information concerning state and city funds, that the advocates for the mentally ill can claim that in three or four years there will be a doubling of homeless, mentally ill people. We used to be a God fearing country but we have seen the atheistic trend of society, with the "me" generation and secular humanistic behavior rising. Caring for others has become a job that no one wants.

Even though the funds were not in place, the advocates of the mentally ill were still insisting that patients were better outside of an institution setting and vehemently opposed anyone who supported keeping the hospital open. It was learned later that a coalition of seven advocate groups for deinstitutionalization would receive over forty million dollars to assist in community placements, apartments, boarding homes, etc. One of the advocate groups was headed by a former mental patient, Jim Smith. He wanted the hospital to close and showed his determination to achieve this goal.

These groups were advantageous to the politicians who wanted to secure these grounds for the land developers. They could do some of the dirty work for the politicians without knowing it. They would be used as a tool of government without realizing it.

A social worker, voicing his opinion–as well as that of the family groups–stated that the patients who remained here were the terminally ill and would be better off here. He also stated that Mr. Smith knew nothing of what he was talking about, as the director had no knowledge or experience in dealing with the care and treatment of these patients. His view was one-sided, as seen from that of a patient. Mr. Randall also tried to convince Mr. Smith that the best thing for the community was for the hospital to remain open. The confrontation between these two personalities began.

Mr. Randall had published many articles in a community newspaper in his continuing crusade to stop the closure of Westmont. The administrators were very annoyed with any opposition to their plans.

The wife of a former president at a state-wide organization for families of the mentally ill who was strangled by her mentally ill son at her home. The boy had suffered from schizophrenia for more than ten years. Now he was charged with homicide and jailed without bail.

Mrs. Pisano and her husband were considered pioneers in the growing advocacy movements among families of the mentally ill, and helped found the "Alliance for the Mentally Ill" of Pennsylvania in 1983. This organization lobbied with the "National Alliance for the Mentally Ill" for improvements in the state mental health services.

After killing his mother, Fred Pisano was calm and coopera- tive with the arresting police officers. He seemed coherent but didn't realize what he was saying. He had been living at home for seven months, and his parents thought that his behavior had become better and more appropriate over time. Fred had lived in four different group homes over the past ten years but they did not help. Mr. Pisano admitted that, "Basically, the services were not out there and not geared for the severely mentally ill."

Fred was arrested twice for attacking staff members during the community placements. In 1986, he was again arrested for assaulting a counselor, striking her twenty times across the face. In 1987, he was arrested after striking a case manager several times with his fists and was released from jail one year later.

Even at home, Fred's behavior was problematic at times. The mentally ill son was living in the basement of his parent's home. He always blasted the stereo until the walls shook from the vibra- tions. Although he could not play or read music, he would strum along on a broken guitar. On this particular evening, he returned to the basement after dinner and turned the stereo on to its maximum volume. Fred had also refused to take his medication after dinner. Mrs. Pisano descended the stairway and started to quarrel with him about the loudness of the stereo, and also scolded him for not taking his medication after dinner.

Fred then punched his mother, knocking her to the floor, and proceeded to strangle her. He boasted that he gave her a "right cross." He realized that, after this act, jail was inevitable, so he proceeded to "do it right." He strangled her until she lost conscious- ness; he then stood up and stepped on her throat. Sneaker marks were found imprinted on her neck by the coroner. Fred then tied a T-shirt around his mother's neck and "polished her off," he arro- gantly told the police. He also stated that he had been afraid that modern technology would revive her.

The official cause of death was asphyxiation, multiple broken ribs and internal bleeding. Fred had thought about killing his mother several times before because she "bugged" him about his music.

He also had delusions that he had formed a band, although he could not read a note of music. He imagined that his mother wouldn't let him marry, although he did not have a girlfriend.

As stated previously, schizophrenics are unpredictable–you never know what will trigger their violent behavior. You also cannot predict what is in their minds. In this case no one suspected Fred's hostility and hatred toward his mother's attention and scoldings and, being uninhibited because of his illness, killed her spontaneously without previous signs or intentions. The killing was not premeditated; rather, he acted on impulse when his hostilities toward her reached a boiling point.

The Pisanos believed in the community mental health system–that the mentally ill could function in the "real world" and not be "warehoused" in state hospitals. Mrs. Pisano was going to prove that it could work!

No one can understand the mentally ill unless they are exposed to them in a professional setting. Only experience in caring and treating these afflicted individuals can help someone gain real insight to the unpredictability of the situations that could arise at any time. By monitoring these patients on a day-to-day basis, one can learn to recognize a particular idiosyncrasy which may lead to a violent act and act on this knowledge to prevent such events.

The consumer advocates can only recognize symptoms brought out in their own cases since everyone reacts differently in a given situation. Because many consumer advocates take their medications and can function well in the community setting, they believe that if it happened for them, it can happen for all. But this is simply not true!

Mr. Pisano sat at his kitchen table while being interviewed, peering at all of the documents relating to his son's illness. His only words at the time were, "In my heart, he's still my son. In my mind, he killed my wife!"

Fred will never be allowed to return home again, and even though Mr. Pisano felt obligated to Fred at a father, it would be difficult seeing and talking to him. Mr. Pisano insisted that he would continue to fight for his son's cause and would continue with his wife's struggle.

Fred's violent, assaultive past history had proven that there was no place in the community for him. His frequent expulsions from community group homes, which always seemed precipitated by assaults and injuries to staff and peers, should accentuate the need for an environment which is protective of the patient and community alike.

Mrs. Pisano never gave up; she was tireless in her efforts to try and obtain employment for her son, monitoring his medications and maintaining contact with his case workers. She was tenacious and never gave up her lifetime cause, and now she was dead!

As stated previously, schizophrenics are unpredictable and you never know what can trigger them: it could be a word; it could be a condition; it could be a person who reminds them of someone they don't like; it could be anything!

Ethel Richter and Jim Smith were in her office one morning and decided to call Mr. Randall and see if they could incite him on the phone. While Mr. Randall and Jim were speaking, Ethel was listening in on her extension. Jim was purposely trying to goad Mr. Randall into some sort of anger, but Mr. Randall maintained a calm, controlled voice while, nevertheless, getting his point across. The conspirators said that Randall verbally threatened Jim on the phone, stating that he would break both of Jim's legs if he should come on the ward. Randall denied this allegation. This was enough for a suspension, they said, and now they could rid themselves of a pest.

I asked Mr. Randall to elaborate on the conversation that lead to his suspension and specify the details:

Randall: "You are not an employee here and you do not understand what goes on here, nor do you know the difference in treatments or therapies. You have a distorted view of how to care for these people. Being mentally ill yourself does not qualify you to make statements and, therefore, you should not even be involved with the decision making process since you are only confusing the matter."
Smith: "What do you mean by saying these things? I know what I'm talking about, and these patients will be cared for better in the community!"
Randall: "This hospital is a necessity. What we are offering here in terms of care cannot be duplicated in the community. These patients are hospitalized for a reason. This is not a place where people are treated then leave! This is the end of the line for many of them! This is the last resort! The remaining patients, for the most

part, are the chronic mental patients. I'm sure that you know what I'm talking about, being a patient once yourself and living in an institution for almost ten years."

Smith: "You don't know! I'm cured now and I want to help other mental patients! You only want the hospital to stay open so that you won't lose your job!" Mr. Smith's voice was becoming excited and loud and appeared to be escalating with anger.

Randall: "I care about you, and you need help instead of trying to help." Randall's voice continued to remain calm and steady. "Do you really believe that alternatives should be placed in high crime areas instead of being surrounded by a nice campus?"

Smith: "We've got to close Westmont down! The state is too kind to these irresponsible, incompetent employees!"

Randall: "As I said before, you don't understand what you're talking about. Schizophrenia is only controlled, not cured."

Smith: "The staff is trying to sabotage the deinstitutionalization program. We've seen the sabotage efforts! I heard enough from you, and I'll be around!

Randall: "Not if I can help it." And with that last remark, Mr. Smith slammed down the phone.

Mr. Smith was diagnosed as "schizophrenic, paranoid type" and, at the age of nineteen, started showing traits of his illness. He had walked naked in the streets clad only in a sheet and suffered from audio and visual hallucinations, swearing that the radio and television were calling his name. His colorful past included roaming the streets, hospitalizations and homelessness.

Naturally the state officials involved with the patient phaseout program appreciated Smith's input and encouraged it. He was another tool used for the closure of Westmont.

Later that same month, after Randall's suspension, Randall, Smith and family members participated in a talk radio show. Smith behaved so badly that the host of the show had him escorted from the studio. It was learned later that he had made an obscene gesture and would not behave properly. When the show ended and Randall went home, he received notice from the hospital that he was fired! This was the way that the state would rid itself of opposition. Mr. Randall had sixteen years invested in the state system and, unless reinstated, he would lose his pension and benefits. His working record was very good, and he had never been disciplined before. He was a dependable employee and always worked for the welfare of his patients and their families.

Randall's dismissal only induced anger among staff, patients and families. Grace Applegate, as enraged as the others, wrote a letter to a neighborhood paper about the discharging of patients into the community and the methods being used to accomplish this task. It was not possible to write to The Quest for they would not publish anything harmful to the officials who were closing Westmont. This letter stated that patients who were known rapists, arsonists, pedophiles and promiscuous were listed for releases. The administrators disagreed with her statements whole-heartedly and yet, when questioned by the reporter, said they could not dispute the statements because they were not familiar with the patients' histories. However, they continued, it could be true since they do not hold patients prisoner. When they are cured of their psychosis, they are, naturally, released.

The Applegate letter was passed around to the staff members to guarantee consensus before it was mailed. One hundred twenty-five signatures were easily obtained without asking anyone to sign. Everyone was disgusted and said the facts were true, and that she had put into words exactly how they felt.

As stated previously, the city newspaper would not publish any adverse opinions sent to it. Letters to the editor were hardly ever seen in print so that the public would not gain knowledge of this placement plan. The Quest only knew how to print "Abuse, Neglect, Irresponsibility and Incompetence."

Administrators were not pleased when the letter appeared in the community press, and told the media that the patients, staff and families had input into the evaluations and proper channels of patient placements. To back up their statements, they obtained time on the local television station and told the public how wonderful everything was going and that the CTT members were following up patient placements very carefully.

The Quest had a reporter call Applegate and ask for more information, as she had contacted the neighborhood edition and they wanted part of the action. She denied this for fear of loss of her job, as well as the feeling she had that they only wanted to use her. Mrs. Applegate expected to be called down on this and she waited for the response by the administration. Two weeks after the publication of her article, her superior approached Mrs. Applegate in her office, closing the door behind her. Uh-oh. This is it!

Before her boss could say anything, Mrs. Applegate quoted

the first amendment, which guarantees freedom of speech. She stated that before becoming a state employee, she was a United States citizen and what she had said was on her own time and in her own home. She also stated that she was not living in Nazi Germany or KGB Russia.

It was brought to her attention that if she was unhappy, she should have gone "upward," not outward, and should have used the system. Mrs. Applegate said, "To who: Booker, Richter, Knight of Mr. Whitman? These are the people creating this situation." One thing lead to another, but it was quite clear that any more opposition or expressions of disapproval would be dealt with in possibly the same route as Mr. Randall–by harassment, intimidation, discipline or entrapment. Mrs. Applegate knew the implications of further activity. This is one reason why many cannot oppose their government without reprisals of job loss or cuts in retirement funds and other benefits.

It is hard to believe that in America we are still restrained–to an extent–when politics are involved. When dealing in human life, and not products or bundles of wheat, one cannot control the feelings of concern and care for another human being.

Families became loud and boisterous, condemning the state's program of deinstitutionalization, stating that they were not informed of their loved ones'' destinies. A lawyer was obtained to get an injunction to stop the method of discharging, and they now called their group "Protect The Patients" family support group. With this dissention they were no longer invited to meet on hospital grounds. Further meetings were held–if not at the hospital, then in a church, hotel or whatever facility would host them.

The family support group was beneficial to all and existing problems and fears united them even closer. They all held the same interests and concerns for their relatives. They had the same theory as Alanon, or drug rehab programs, and their problems coincided with one another's. Letters were constantly written to the city's only newspaper, The Quest, condemning the treatment of families, the exodus of patients and the inhumane conception of placement, but to no avail–these letters were never printed or acknowledged. the public would remain ignorant of the state's "Bold Plan of Deinstitutionalization." This meant that the governor and the mayor had the support of the newspaper. Had it not supported both candidates at election time? Is not the news media a great influence on public opinion?

A church offered the families their recreation hall for their meeting, as they sympathized with the families and realized what the state was doing and the hardships it was causing. The only condition which had to be met was that the use of the church hall for their meeting would not be publicized.

The meeting was held there, and all of the families left the room as they had found it, placing the chairs and tables in exactly the same place that they had found them. All of the lights were shut off, and the key was returned to the church. They wanted to be able to return if needed. On a Sunday previous to that meeting, the family support group had rented a hotel room for $150 to assemble and discuss their family problems collectively. Continued support came from both outsiders and other family members who united with them. Mr. Randall and Mr. Formbe, the father of one of the patients, conducted and organized the families and the meetings.

CHAPTER THREE

Thirty-one years ago a child was born. Little did this creature know that he would not be a blessing to someone but just another misfortune in the life of a prostitute who indulged herself in all of life's sexual pleasures. The mother of William consorted with gamblers, and it is believed that she married one of them and that he was William's father. The tragedy of this birth was only one of six that his mother had. Yes! She had six children and all with different fathers. William was the last child born to this woman who had undergone numerous abortions during her lifetime. His mother lost her life due to an illegal abortion when William was only four years old. Would he have been better off if he had been one of them? After reading this history, you may come to answer this question!

The other five children conceived by this woman would also have problems: one ended up with a criminal record and was placed in jail for shoplifting; one was placed in another institution with emotional problems; one sister overdosed and died at the age of nineteen from heroin; one was jailed for assault and robbery; the other two sisters probably lead normal lives, as there were no history records to report on their backgrounds.

William's mother placed him in a day care center at the age of three months but did not return for him for a period of six weeks while she continued her night life of self-indulgence. When he was eight months old, she again took him to the day care center where it was discovered that he was suffering from a high fever, dehydration, malnutrition and emaciation. Anyone could see the neglect and abuse, and it was evident that she had not fed him properly or even changed his diapers.

She abandoned him there and appeared only sporadically–perhaps only out of curiosity–for it was apparent that she did not love anyone but herself. All of the children except William were cared for by the Department of Welfare and placed into foster homes.

Mrs. Richards, who ran the day care center, adopted William at the age of four years after his mother had passed away. She and her husband could never have children of their own, and William could fill the void in their lives. He filled the void alright, but with nothing but emotional and behavioral problems.

He was an unhappy child whose extensive crying indicated a problem of some sort. He began nursery school at the age of two and one-half and kindergarten at the age of four and one-half. He appeared to be very bright in the first grade, but was continually experiencing behavior problems such as crying, hiding and stealing school items. His adoptive parents said that he was "devilish and teasing." By the end of the third grade, it was recommended that he receive psychiatric treatment and the decision was to "transfer [him] to a private school." In the fourth grade, he was transferred to Larkwood Boy's Academy, where he would only remain for one and one-half years before complaints arose of severe headaches and "unreasonable punishment."

When William was eleven, he was transferred to Redhill Academy, where he spent only five months before he was expelled for more behavioral problems such as destroying school furniture, spray painting walls and hiding.

He continued to experience headaches, dizziness and weakness, and was taken out of school. Perhaps a vacation was what he needed! The family packed up and traveled throughout North America, but his complaints continued.

When they returned home from their vacation, William was placed into a general hospital for observation, at which time it was determined that he might have been suffering from Petit Mal seizures.

A feeling of hopelessness was starting to fester in the anxieties of this loving, adoptive parental relationship. William never knew that his parents had adopted him until someone told him when he was eight years old. He felt tormented, lost and abandoned. He wondered what his mother looked like and why she went away. What was wrong with him? Why didn't she want him? William never knew his father.

Now enrolled in public school, hopes were high that William could achieve better grades in a less restrictive environment. He ran away from home shortly after enrollment. His tangled, tortured, tormented mind gave him a feeling of uselessness and low self-esteem. He wondered, "Why was everyone trying to get rid of me?" First his mother, then the private schools, etc.

There were many periods of starvation or compulsive eating. William was a very disturbed child. When William ran away, he ended up in the Stanley Child Care Center, where he remained for one and one-half years before he was admitted to the general hospital for unsteadiness, dizziness and malnutrition. After his discharge he returned home, but only for a short period of time before explosive behaviors surfaced with threats of burning down his parents' home. William was again admitted to the general hospital and, from there, was transferred to a psychiatric center and then to Westmont.

He would be known as recidivistic, being admitted at least six different times. Due to his assaultiveness and destructive behavior, he was transferred to another state institution which was equipped with special "Assaultive Management Programs." He remained there for five months, displaying several explosive episodes as well as three suicide attempts.

When admitted to Westmont, he was diagnosed with Under-socialized Aggressive Disorder and Temporal Lobe Epilepsy. Work history was nil except for a short term of employment in a warehouse which ended in termination due to the severity of William's destructive behavior.

Upon the death of his adoptive father, William's mother could no longer tolerate his behaviors and numerous admissions and regressions, and soon stopped all contact with William and Westmont.

William was being considered for placement in the community and was placed in discharge planning. Because there had not been any destruction since September, 1988, and he appeared to be controlling his frustrations and anger, he had been given full ground privileges. In an episode last September, it became necessary to restrain William after he had broken every window, light fixture and in furniture in the lobby. At that time it required fifteen male staff members to control him. He lost control easily, and hostilities could be triggered during sports or games when his team leaned toward the loss column. He could also lose his cool if his demands weren't immediately met. He could not accept his own feelings of frustration nor could he feel comfortable in a structured environment.

Mr. Tweedil, an advocate for the mentally ill, took William to seek an apartment for possible placement into the community. Even though William played along with the idea, his mind was in turmoil and he tried to hide his fears and anxieties inside. He had often stated that he couldn't make it in the outside world!

Since he was a small boy, something had driven him to anger and he would vent his frustrations by destroying property, which seemed to give him instant gratification. He never worried about the consequences of such behavior. Perhaps a feeling of a lost realistic environment and family combined with the number of lifetime rejections sparked these irate feelings.

The closer the reality of placement appeared, the more his anxieties built up and, once again, the destructive, assaultive behavior reared its ugly head. The thought of community placement appeared to be a threat to his security, as he had never existed in society. He appeared so frightened of placement that he again displayed destruction of property; but this time he attacked a staff member, hitting him with a broken neon lighting tube and causing scratches and abrasions about the man's head.

William was once again put in four-point restraints due to suicidal threats and his statement that "I'll take someone with me!" He displayed more paranoid traits, claiming that one tour didn't care about him and was mean, while the other tour catered to his whims. He was verbally threatening, stating, "I'll kill someone; I'll kill you; I'll see you later!" William started spitting at the staff while in restraints and had ripped the mattress open, pulling out the filling until the springs were exposed.

He would try to manipulate the staff and try to bargain for the release of one hand restraint: "If you only put me in three-point instead of four-point restraints, I'll let you change the mattress and I'll go to sleep." Even if you think that a mental patient is bluffing, you can never trust your intuition. They can be very manipulative.

William's eyes were fiery, and he was sitting up in bed. This was possible although he was restrained, as the arms and legs would protect staff from being injured on an impulse of anger or revenge. It also would protect him from self-harm. There was no way that he would listen to any verbal intervention. He had also refused to take his P.R.N. medication. He finally accepted it but the anger was still evident in the facial twists and expressions.

William was well over six feet tall and was very strong. We could not take the chance, in the state of mind that he was in, to release him for any reason unless adequate staff was present. He would be kept in four points all night!

And this episode too would pass. He would again at some time regain his grounds when his behavior became appropriate. This man could never exist in a societal setting and, at this time, it would be ridiculous to think so. He would probably continue this type of behavior for the remainder of his life, unless science or research could produce another alternative or trend toward treatment. How could William fit into a behavior modification program? Nothing else had ever worked for him!

Marvin Hall, who had been discharged through the courts, continued to call his old ward. He had been hospitalized for so long that he probably had no outside friends or contacts. There were never any visitors or interested family that we knew about. He had no work history listed, nor did he have any known hobbies. Marvin was a little on the lazy side and never wanted to work in the prep shop to earn monies of his own. He was receiving a small amount of money each month, and that seemed to satisfy him. He would spend the money himself the first day, of else he would give it away to the other patients. He related well with his peers and there were never reports of conflict with any of them. These were his buddies and the staff was his family. This had been his home! by all of the frequent phone calls he made, it was clear to the staff that we were his family and the familiar voices were consoling to him. What troubled the staff was a conversation threatening suicide by jumping in front of a train. We didn't know where he was calling from and there was no address listed for him. After several months, the phone calls stopped. We never knew whether or not he had succeeded.

Mary Wasso, a forty-one year old woman with schizophrenia of at least a twenty year duration, was admitted to Westmont on five different occasions during the past four years for recurrences of severe schizophrenic episodes. All of her hospital admissions were brought about by bizarre behaviors: disrobing in the streets; yelling and screaming; neglect of personal hygiene and appearance; evidence of poor nutrition, etc. Upon admission she demonstrated a severe thought disturbance, with marked suspicion and misinterpretations of things happening around her. During remissions she displayed impaired judgment and needed support from those around her to interpret reality. When she wasn't receiving these supports, she could withdraw into her own autistic universe.

Larry Hart was a twenty-five year old man with paranoid schizophrenia. At the age of twenty-two, poor grades and lack of motivation forced him to drop out of college. During his high school years, he had been an outstanding student and athlete. Classmates held high hopes for him; that he would, most of all, he a success in life. He was energetic and enthusiastic with any assignment given him. He was well-liked and was considered to have a dynamic personality.

He became involved in substance abuse and began thinking that people were avoiding him and that strangers were aware of his inner thoughts. He became delusional, believing that his body carried a transmitter and that people were spying on him. At this point he responded to internal stimuli and believed that voices were calling to him. A friend notified his parents of this peculiar behavior. They immediately arranged for Larry to be hospitalized in Westmont. After continued treatment and therapy, he was able to return to the community and found employment as a clerk in a real estate office. There he met a woman and they became romantically involved. He began living with her, but never divulged his psychiatric history. It is not known if he continued with his medication routine or if he had returned for more hospitalization at another facility.

When returning to communities, many patients only comply sporadically with attendance to a community health center and, eventually, their conditions begin to deteriorate; hence, readmission to the hospital setting recurs. Some patients cease their medications due to side effects such as Tardive Dyskenesia, tongue rolling and hand tremors. Some symptoms of Parkinsonism appear. The consensus of physicians is that a patient with schizophrenia will probably have a history of relapse and repeated hospitalizations.

As patients were discharged or transferred to assessment center, the staff was also being depleted in all disciplines. As there was a demand for male psychiatric aides, they were the first to be transferred to other facilities in the state. They were even given promotions to justify the transfers. No one would be able to contest the transfers when they were being done in this manner. Who could hold up promotions? In fact they did not have to choose who to promote this time; it could have been on hold until Westmont closed.! Female staff members felt the discrimination, as many of them had more seniority than most of the promoted males. The wards, depleted of staff, were becoming a threat to the remaining staff. More incidents of staff injuries occurred, which resulted in more disability leaves. This would short the wards even more! The patients were ill, not stupid. They recognized the shortage of staff and acted out more frequently. This would then require a stat call for manpower from other wards.

Psychiatric aides also left the staff to join the CTT program This program was guaranteed funding for a two year period. What would happen after two years if funds were not renewed? The orientation program for the CTT teams produced much enthusiasm and a willingness to start the follow-up procedures. Many of the members of the CTT were "gung-ho," but after four to six months, many became disillusioned, and some left the program. They were on twenty-four hour call and were expected to retrieve their clients from bars–or out of town if necessary–if their assigned patient happened to wander off. Some of their clients were housed in apartments in poor, drug-infested neighborhoods. Each member carried a beeper for emergencies concerning their clients.

One male nurse was mugged by three men who confiscated his wallet while on a mission. Dave, the nurse, was really shook, as there was no way out and he could not escape because they had him surrounded. "I'm a nurse," he told them. "I don't have any drugs or syringes, either. Please take my money, but return my wallet," he asked excitedly. It was only because he had thirty dollars that they let him go; but if the amount of money had been less than that, they may have killed him.

The safety of the staff and clients was not considered in the program, as danger always lurks in the inner urban community, known for its crime and drug abuse.

Other disciplines–recreational therapists, social workers, housekeepers, maintenance and garage workers–were slowly transferred or furloughed. The hospital closing, which was originally scheduled for December, 1989, was suddenly moved up to June 30. It was also rumored that the administrators of the hospital and the top state official and his staff would receive large bonuses if closure was achieved by that date. There must have been some truth in the rumor, because it appeared that the patient transfers were speeded up.

Charts were pulled over to the administration building on a daily basis by Lois Booker, who seemed to be the person in charge of the transfers. Wards were given transfer notices one day, or often the evening, before the move was to occur. There was no time for proper preparation, and the families were not notified when these decisions were made. Some patients were uprooted from Westmont and sent to the Rothman Center for further evaluations and assessments. Other patients were sent to another general psychiatric hospital wing for the same purpose. And still others were discharged to a half-way house which was located in a traffic-congested area near a river. There were no beautiful grounds to walk on. There was no corner store for the patients to purchase their little pleasures, such as soda, candy and cigarettes. They would no longer be free to walk around as they were at Westmont.; Most would be confined to the wards in these places for evaluation.

As one group of patients returned to Westmont from these centers, others were sent in their place. Many stated that they were glad to be back. Some families complained of the places their relatives had been sent to. The state was playing "ring around the rosey," or a live game of checkers, with the lives of these human beings. In the game of checkers, pieces are removed from the board. The big difference was that the patients were returning and the census was remaining the same.

The patients who returned appeared to be decomposing due to experimentation with medication while at their centers. Upon return diagnoses were mostly unchanged, and the new evaluations were not much different than the ones received at Westmont.

One center doing the evaluations was receiving $420 per patient per day. No wonder they wanted to remain at full capacity. The other hospital facility was given a grant of $7.5 million to do the same process.

There were reports of hostile, aggressive behaviors from the patients with injuries to doctors, staff and others at these facilities. Patients who were discharged to the half-way house often eloped and ended up as street people. They were often seen downtown by staff members.

One patient attacked a female staff member and attempted to rape her. He was taken to a detention center. Another patient from Westmont, Mary Logan–who was known to have suicidal tendencies–was discharged to the half-way house. While in Westmont she was placed on a one-to-one many times to prevent self-injury. This meant that one person would remain within an arm's length at all times to prevent self-harm. Mary wandered away from this center and was seen by a passer-by attempting to jump from a well-known bridge before she was rescued.

Since the beginning of these placement operations, the state only had placed five patients in a six month period. The state was becoming frustrated because the remaining patients were the hard-core mentally ill and could not be placed easily. These are the patients with long histories of psychiatric treatment and hospitalizations, who had not responded to medications, interventions, recreational activities or social programs. These were the patients who families could not manage them at home, with some memories of fearful experiences remaining fresh in their minds. These are the patients who were recidivistic in communities, boarding homes and half-way houses, and who were not compliant with medications and relapsed into their illness time and time again.

The patients who were appropriate, and who responded to treatment, were the patients who were discharged from the institution. Deinstitutionalization is not for all. There are those who may never function appropriately for community living, and will continue to require a structured living environment.

When the land deal was made for Westmont, there was continuous denial from both the administrators and the Department of Public Welfare. Why were the gas and telephone companies digging up the street in front of the hospital grounds and laying pipe lines? Why were more hotels and motels being built around the area? Why would the state now spend monies to plant a flower bed on the main road to dress up the front grounds? Why were surveyors seen many times on the grounds? Why was the state in such a hurry to close the wards and buildings, only to fill the other wards? Why did the surrounding community hold a meeting hosted by land developers in a nearby school? Why did these developers place large charts on the wall, shaded in various colors, showing the divisions of the hospital land? Why did they pass out questionnaires to see if the neighbors wanted a medical building, cultural center, shopping mall, condominiums, etc?

Not one word was directed toward the fate of patients already existing on the grounds. This proved that there was no concern for these afflicted people. No one asked, "What will happen to the patients?" As stated in the preface, the public does not want to know.

The hospital had stood there for eighty years, even before houses were built in that area. These same neighbors, who purchased these homes knowing full well that the hospital was there wanted the hospital closed. This is another example of the mentally ill being treated as "less than human." In the twenty to twenty-five years that the hospital had been there, no one had ever been injured by a patient. The neighborhood children used the grounds to ride bikes, jog, play basketball, etc., and no one had ever been hurt. The neighbors walked their dogs there at regular intervals. Yes! These grounds were already utilized by the community.

While listening to the talk radio station during the latter part of May, 1989, a woman called in and questioned: "What are they going to do with the empty buildings at Westmont? Are they waiting for them to be vandalized? Are they going to tear them down now that the patients are all gone?"

"I don't know," the host of the show answered.

A staff member at Westmont became furious when she heard this and called the station.

"Hello, my name is Florence, and I'm calling you from Westmont. I want you to know that we are still here and that the patients are still here."

"Hang on, you're next," said the producer, who also surprised to find that the hospital was still open.

The public was not informed that the hospital was still open and in service, with several hundred patients still on the premises.

No one asked, and no one cared!

Florence told the radio host that the remaining patients were the hard-core mentally ill, and that the state had not been able to successfully place them.

The families of these patients were petitioning their state representatives to keep three buildings, all located on one street of the hospital grounds, open. They stated that the land developers could have the remaining acreage for development. They requested that the state leave this small portion of land, with existing buildings, for the patients and their families.

The governor had publicly stated in the latter days of April that he would be glad to meet with the families to discuss their problems. The families waited and waited, but no meeting was ever arranged for them. They believed that this was only a political gesture, made under pressure at the time because of concern about the closure of Westmont. After a reasonable amount of time, the families began to call his office to ask when this meeting, about which he had spoken publicly, would take place.

When this statement was made by the governor, the families had called him and his staff "assassins" because many of the patients who were pushed out, either by the courts or through discharges, had bad experiences–there were even reports of some deaths. The governor was never available to speak with them; they spoke either with his secretary or an assistant. He could never be reached personally.

Mr. Formbe and Mr. Randall, along with other family members, personally contacted and met with several state representatives. Their first response was one of sympathy to their problem, and the families received assurance that, "We will do all that we can!" All of the legislators had the same response, but no action was ever taken and they were never quoted in the newspaper.

The lawyers that the families engaged seemed to also be stalemated, and the feelings among the staff and families were that the state must by paying them off as well. But they were determined that Westmont would close!

Why the rush? We are dealing with human beings, not products! Why not do things right and take the proper time for families and patients to adjust to the closure and possible transfers to other state institutions? Why was a time schedule given to the land developers by the state?

The bold plan of economics was a failure. Monies spent on overtime to staff the wards were astronomical. It would have been cheaper to give state benefits to the temporary staff. The regular staff was depleted and patient activities were cut; housekeepers were trying to keep up with the overload of work; maintenance was delayed for emergencies; kitchen and dining rooms closed, the food trays were delivered from another state institution and patients were eating in the dayrooms on the wards; mail delivery was delayed; examples of the waste go on and one.

On paper it appeared that we were closed but, in reality, the patients were all here!

Monies spent on transportation for the CTT involved the purchase of at least one dozen new station wagons. Apartment rents and utilities had to be met. Some staff members stayed around the clock in apartments with placed patients who were assaultive, destructive and inappropriate; windows were broken out on a daily basis and replaced by the staff; supermarkets and drug stores wrecked by the patients, which the state was forced to reimburse, were all added expenses not compiled in the estimated costs of caring for patients in the community.

There was never any negative publicity about the placement program; rather, there were televised appearances by Ms. Knight, Deputy Secretary of Welfare, stating how wonderful the placement program was functioning. She had visions of closing Westmont with all of the patients doing well in the community. But now even the advocates for the mentally ill were having second thoughts. With the number of disturbing incidents occurring, and the state and city disputing over monies to be paid by each to support this program, they were becoming very discouraged.

Attorneys for the patients urged a delay in the closing of Westmont, stating that the community services were not in place for the patients who needed them. This request was presented to a United Stated district judge.

They acquired an injunction to halt the closure a year ago and, one year later, it has still never been formally introduced in the courts. It was learned that the judge was of the same political party as the governor, and that the judge backed him 100 percent. The governor was the one delaying the process. Of course this would never be admitted publicly.

The families were told that it was on the agenda several months ago. Remember–the families often did not want their identities known, as they felt that it would stigmatize other family members. For this reason they did not wish to appear in public and thus never received the public coverage they needed.

Often the questions were asked by someone: "What ever happened to the injunction that the families were trying to obtain to halt the closing and the transfers of these patients?"; "What is taking them so long?"; "Why didn't this case have a hearing yet?"; "Is the state paying the courts off, too?"; "When are they going to act, and when will we know the outcome–when it's too late?"

Even the Director of Mental Retardation and Mental Health had thought that the September date was too soon. Programs were either inadequate or non-existent for many groups of patients, such as the drug and alcohol abusers, Organic Brain Syndrome sufferers (due to brain injuries which caused damages), those people who exhibit non-criminal but unacceptable social behaviors, such as inappropriateness toward the opposite sex, and, lastly, the mentally retarded.

One advocate placed the blame on the state. He stated that the reality is that years of state mismanagement and neglect are the real causes of Westmont's demise. Abandon and then blame the victim. The problems namely are a fundamental failure by public officials to appreciate the complexities of the problems of the mentally ill [and] the lack of mental health systems that fully integrate state hospital care with community support systems.

"Has the hard-core mental psychiatric in-patient treatment suddenly become less of a need in this city?" Eisenhith asked. The state allows thousands of former hospital patients to deteriorate in boarding homes, prisons and on the streets."

Because the census was not lowered as easily as it was thought it could be, it became necessary to extend the closure of Westmont until September. Families were meeting with some state representatives to protest the closing. They were also calling Booker, Knight and Whitman, threatening legal action if their relatives were moved without their knowledge. Westmont should remain open! Even at this point, Mary Knight again appeared on television to assure the public that the patients would be cared for and followed-up by the CTT members. She would not admit defeat. Isn't it amazing that the media gave the state so much coverage and the families could not get to first base in presenting their case?

Rumors again floated around the hospital that the administrators were planning mass-busing on one day to another state institution. If this were done without publicity or family knowledge, they could by-pass the lawyers and then pay them off later. It would then be too late for protest and the bonuses would still be in effect. This could be possible, as nurses were already transferred to another facility and the Bridging Plan came into effect.

Because the administration had cried wolf about the loss of nursing staff, nurses were sent to Westmont each Sunday from other state hospitals. It was not brought out that agency nurses and staff nurses doing overtime covered the wards quite well. These bridge nurses were sent to motels and hotels with meal allowances, plus time and one-half status while working at Westmont. They would also recover travel time and miles traveled by their own cars. Most would be assigned to wards with other nurses who continued to train them. When the end of the week came, many went back to their own hospitals and, on the next Sunday, it would start all over again. The bridge nurses were paid from budgets in their own hospital cost centers.

Their time schedules would be faxed back to their own hospitals. On paper in the state's capitol, these bridge nurses did not appear as Westmont staff members. It would seem as if a nurse shortage really did exist.

These bridge nurses were resented by the regular staff. The ward nurses were often displaced from their regular wards, only to be replaced by the bridge nurses. It wasn't really the nurses they resented but the plan itself. These nurses were told at their hospitals how rough it would be to work here because Westmont was known to be nasty and mean. They were afraid that their tires would be slashed, and the husbands of nurses did not want them to come her.

When they did arrive, they were amazed a the courtesy they received and stated that this was not what they had expected. The reputation which Westmont had been given by the press extended further than we had expected. They liked the atmosphere, and often stated that, in some ways, our hospital was very similar to theirs. Some stated that it was nicer.

It was clear that the state was wasting money. No matter whose budget the monies were drawn from, the taxpayers were the losers. The cost for care of the mentally ill at Westmont was estimated to be thirty-one million dollars per year. The governor announced that $140 million would be spent on a new drug program; another $13 million to fix a market terminal; $1.6 billion (yes, billion) would be given to the education department. This looked like a misprint and was read over and over again. Yes! The Quest had mentioned this amount in several different places within the news article. It was not a misprint. With all of these expenditures, there were no monies to keep these patients in a safe, structured environment. It is only too clear that the mental patient was expendable. The answer must be the value of these grounds. Considering the great population of this big city, and that most patients come from poor, deprived neighborhoods, the state was shirking its responsibility to care for its citizens. Where are their human rights? Where are the family's rights to chose where their relatives should be placed if not Westmont?

Summer in many state hospitals was another horrible experience. When the weather was sweltering and remained in the nineties for a prolonged period of time, the brick buildings heated up and would hold the heat in like a brick oven even after the weather had cooled on the outside. Think about it–living in this heat day and night without relief. At least the staff could go home after their tour of duty and cool off, but the mental patients had to endure the entire summer in hot dormitories. It was only recently that the dayrooms were air conditioned, but the remainder of the wards and dormitories were not.

Fans were blowing and humming as you entered the wards or nursing offices. At times the noise factor from these fans was so great that conversations were eliminated until one or two were turned off. The air was turbulent and was always warm to hot, with temperatures often reaching ninety or above on the wards and never decreasing at night.

Patients receiving the psychotropic medications were already predisposed to become dehydrated quicker than other people.

The administration offered several ways to fight the heat: Take the ward temperatures and record them on your reports every tour (does this really solve the dilemma or cool the wards? or is this just curiosity?); Give extra fluids to the patients to prevent dehydration; Give more showers to overheated patients; Observe patients for weakness, etc. But never did any of the administrators request air conditioning or petition the state to obtain it. There were many air conditioners in the rooms of the administration building, and their meetings were held in comfort.

The pharmacy was air conditioned because the drugs had to be kept cool so they would not decompose or lose their effect. Rooms where the Xerox machines were stored had to be kept air conditioned because the machines would break down easily in the heat. The medication rooms were also kept air conditioned.

When exhaustion and weakness was seen in a patient, the doctor would often write an order to keep the patient in the air conditioned day room. When Long Term Care was in service, there were often ten or twelve beds in the day room at one time. The elderly were affected quicker than the younger patients, as many had numerous medical problems as well. The infirmary was also air conditioned, and patients who had a weak spell were sent there. If not to the infirmary, then they were sent to an outside general hospital. All of this could have been avoided if the buildings were air conditioned.

The staff would sit sweating and drinking from their own ice-filled plastic cups with straws protruding from the lids. They were also becoming less tolerant of the situation, although they didn't suffer through the heat for the same length of time that the patients did.

The heat escalated some of the patients' erratic behaviors and more P.R.N. medications were required. You can't take your clothing off in the summer, but you can put more clothing on in the winter.

The survey teams of Medicare, Medicaid, J.C.A.H. Department of Health and even the Blue Ribbon Committee did not address this "Patient Abuse" by the state. During their reviews they always chose an air conditioned room for their wind-up remarks. There were never any deficiencies stated in their round-up reports. You would always hear them say, "The patients come first!; We are only interested in the patient's welfare!; Our first priority is the patients!"

All of the general hospitals are air conditioned–and have been for many years–for the "normal patients," the staff and visitors. It must be a pleasure to go to your place of employment and be comfortable on the job!

Mental patients are not privileged enough to deserve air conditioning. They usually do not object and many wouldn't know how to. They have suffered for years in the heat of summer and probably don't realize that it could be better. Again we can see that they are treated less than human because they do not demand these comforts and wouldn't be listened to anyway. As stated previously, they do not vote or pay taxes!

Approximately four years ago, when the state expanded the forensic unit, monies were spent to air condition that building. Now only that one building would be comfortable. Everyone in that building now benefits, but all of the others are not affected.

Do you think the reason was because these criminals that were sent to mental institutions by the court due to their incompetency to stand trial were considered more like prisoners? Do they deserve more than the mentally ill?

Here are some true facts that could be substantiated by the staff. On one particular day at the end of July, the temperature outside reached ninety-five degrees. The entire day was a hot and humid one, and the staff was glad to go home at the end of their shift. At nine o'clock at night the fans were still blowing. It's a wonder that their motors didn't burn out, as they had been running continuously day and night without being turned off to cool. The ward temperature was 99 degrees and the nursing station was 102 degrees!

59

The only air conditioned part of the building was the day room, but the majority of the patients did not stay in there because they didn't want to be confined to one area. They were pacing back and forth through the corridors, and quite a few had their shirts off. Others walked around with open shirts and still were seen with wet, sweaty shirts. Perhaps the air from the fans appealed to them and stood by them to cool down.

Agitated states were apparent due to the sweltering heat and there was no way to relieve their dilemma. When these conditions existed, more P.R.N.s were required to subdue their anxieties and angers, which appeared to be precipitated by the heat.

In the largest mental health institution in the state of Maine, five deaths occurred in August 1988 during an intense heat wave. These deaths were attributed to the interaction of excessive temperatures and the psychotropic medications. Air conditioning was installed after the fact, as a result of the political implications which could have lead to bad publicity for the encumbent in the elections the following year.

It seems that in all stated, the first reaction of the higher echelon is to fire and remove the superintendent when any catastrophic incident occurs. How convenient it is to place the blame on hospital officials when the fault really lies on underfunding and the lack of concern for mental patients until an incident such as this happens.

In San Bernardino, California, in September 1988, an inmate in Patton State Hospital, twenty-three-year-old Francisco Morphin, was found dead, slumped in a chair. Patton State Hospital is one of two of its kind in California that houses criminals after being charged with violent crimes. Morphin was there for stabbing a racetrack guard.

There was a heat wave in San Bernardino at the time, and temperatures soared to 110 degrees. The air conditioning had not been working in building thirty since the month of June and was reported to be out of order. Morphin's body temperature remained at 104 degrees forty minutes after his death, and it was stated by the toxicologist of that hospital that the 104 degrees was a serious risk for organ damage and that Morphin literally fried to death.

Although security was heavy at the hospital, two staff members, Steve and Arthur, were fired for reporting problems there. They stated that there was not enough staff and that corners were cut in care for these individuals. "There was only time to subdue patients with quick injections," they said.

The cause listed in this death was lithium toxicity. The dose had been increased in July but blood levels had never been checked. Lithium is used in mental health but requires monitoring. The hospital was cited in April for failure to monitor lithium levels, but the director of the hospital was still making excuses and denied that the air conditioning had not been working since June. He stated that in large institutions, "We are going to have errors." Excuses were being made, but no one was being held accountable!

In legal suits against state facilities, no fines are actually paid because institutions such as these are considered the property of the taxpayers and the fines are thus simply symbolic.

The Chief of Psychiatry at Harbor UCLA Medical Center stated that, "We have been slipping and sliding and tumbling about in the field of mental health for the past fifteen to twenty years, and now we are in a free fall situation!" Inmates have no place to go and conditions are becoming worse all the time in many states throughout the country.

The bottom line is money: money to supply the needs, money for maintenance, money for sufficient staffing, etc. Officials have ignored or have changed procedures which exist today.

In April 1989, a leaky roof meant curtains for the auditorium on hospital grounds located in a building specially built for cultural and social activities. This had been the on-grounds theatre and seated 1,200 people. The final curtain had fallen and it was decided by the administration to close the building, as it was too dangerous for the public to use. The ceiling tiles were falling and some problems were also occurring with the lighting fixtures. This building had opened in 1957 at a cost of $1 million, but the state would not invest in any major repairs due to the notice of Westmont's closing. The chapel was located in this building, which housed the auditorium and the Sunday services that were held every week. There were patients who relied on the staff to be able to attend these services. The building was now closed, and the chapel was moved to the basement of one of the other buildings. The atmosphere was not the same. The contractors estimated the cost of repairs to the roof at approximately fifty thousand dollars. The state was preparing to divest itself of this hospital site, and the city was preparing its austerity budget. Neither the state nor the city took positions on the final disposition of who would be responsible to repair the roof or whether it would be torn down when the property was sold. If the purchaser wanted to keep the building, they would have to repair it. In the end it was learned that the state would be the one to have the repairs made. Who knows what changed their mind or what deals were made with the land developers.

The land developers called their program "Westmont Re-use Study" with community workshops. On many occasions neighbors surrounding the area of the hospital met to discuss their opinions about the disposition of the vacated grounds. As mentioned before the land was divided on charts, shaded in various colors, and there were options as to what would be built in each shaded area. A questionnaire was handed out to these neighbors asking their opinions about what they wanted to be built on the land. Some suggestions were a major retail center such as Sears, department stores, an office park or interplex, light industrial or warehouse usage, professional offices for doctors, lawyers or accountants, single family homes, townhouses or twin homes, apartments or condominiums, planned retirement communities, a nursing home, or housing for artists or other activity groups.

No one mentioned the patients already existing on the grounds. The veterans wanted to build a nursing home on Westmont' grounds, stating that a large city needed one in their area and that it should be accessible by public transportation. What about the families of the mentally ill? Shouldn't there be a facility for these people also? Shouldn't these families have access by public transportation as well? Isn't there enough room for both?

CHAPTER FOUR

Deaths of patients were already reported in the community, some by suicide and others by the hand of someone else. Other people were also getting hurt. In one instance a patient who had been diagnosed at the hospital with a very bad heart condition was placed in a second floor apartment with an argumentative, irritable mate. This meant that she had to climb the stairs and be subjected to an individual who could be a contributing factor to precipitation of a heart attack. Sadly, this came to pass. Two months after being placed in that apartment, it was learned that the patient had died there on the fourth of July. The staff felt that she would still be alive if she had remained at the hospital.

Street people and the homeless were increasing as predicted. There really was no place for these hard-core mental patients to go.

Derrick Smith Bey, a volatile, unstable personality described by psychiatric staff and professionals as "violently insane," had been in and out of mental facilities for nearly a decade. Not only was this six foot six black male individual who lifted weights tall and strong, but delicate situations could trigger an explosive, uncontrollable mechanism in his personality that lead to out of control, violent behavior. In many facilities where he was interned he could not be dealt with.

His existence was compounded by an additional problem: He carried the AIDS virus. He would use this as a physical threat to intimidate and threaten the staff by saying, "I'll bite you, I'll hurt you, I'll cut you," etc. Yes! He was considered a loaded gun.

In many of his violent episodes he threatened staff members with the threat of biting them and giving them this deadly infection. No one was able to reason with him when he was in one of these states of mind and risked being attacked, thrown to the floor and pounced upon, with both of his fists flying around their heads and faces.

He attacked a staff member in this manner while at Westmont, which resulted in brain damage, seizures, headaches, dizziness, unbalanced equilibrium and permanent disability for his victim. His jaw was fractured in two places, and he suffered multiple concussions.

An aide reported seeing Bey spit on pieces of bread and handing them to his peers. It seemed as if his attitude was, "If I have AIDS, you'll get it!" It seemed as if he was aware of the consequences of the disease and its inevitable death sentence. He was not only violent, but bitter as well.

Bey had been in and out of correctional and psychiatric institutions since the age of sixteen. He could never control his temper and, in the late seventies, was arrested on many occasions for assaults and robberies.

Today these records, which may indicate any incarcerations and to what degree these crimes were committed, are sealed and unavailable.

In 1981 he was a patient in Farview State Hospital for the criminally insane and was discharged and readmitted at least five times. He was one of the most feared people there and continues his behavior patterns through incidents with staff members and others.

After the incident at Westmont that disabled a staff member for life, no charges were filed but, in April, 1988, a deal was made to remove him from Westmont and place him in another state hospital. The staff there was also leery of his history, as he was considered extremely dangerous. A file was kept there containing all of the various incidents in which he was involved, including his verbal threats to give everyone his disease. He had nothing to lose!

The folder file grew and was nearly two inches thick, but every attempt to maintain his internment was not considered, and he was released in December, 1988, to a community group home. They repeatedly begged that he not be released, but he was still allowed to leave. While at Norristown, he was kept isolated from his peers because of his violent attacks on others and his diagnosis of AIDS. On several occasions it became necessary to call for four or five extra staff member to contain his violent outbursts and restrain these precipitated attacks.

In November, 1988, before his release to the community group home, a court hearing was held in Philadelphia concerning his anticipated release and, again, these records were sealed, and this lack of access to the information would not reveal at that time who was responsible and who made the determination to release him.

The superintendent of Norristown State Hospital declined comment on Bey's release. It is evident to all that the state had mandated his silence and mandated that Bey's case records be sealed.

Bey was seen by one of Westmont's staff working in a fast food chain, handling food and serving it to the public. He was shortly fired from this job because of his volatile manner. Thank God! How would we know whether he had spat in the food that was served to the public. With his known attitude of "Infection for all," this thought is not far-fetched.

At Community Council Catchment Area #4, the group home, he was supposed to be monitored around-the-clock by a team of two male attendants. This personnel, however, had not removed the kitchen knives, which later contributed in the slaying of a police officer. This staff was also afraid of and intimidated by Bey.

The group home was not far from where the slaying took place, a bus terminal being watched by their security force. The officer was fatally slashed in the chest with a kitchen knife, and as the officer fell to the ground, he fired four shots which killed Bey on the spot. The two bodies were found dead on the scene. The court documents in this case were also sealed!

This is a true case of the breakdown of our mental health system: the courts, the state hospital administrations and the community health centers. Even in this last case history–which had the catastrophic result of leaving a chronically ill mental patient and a family man dead–a department head spokesman from the Department of Welfare would continue to state, "He may have moved into recession or remission in the community. We would not have discharged a patient who was known to be a threat to himself or others."

Although an officer was dead, and now his wife and children

would be denied their chance of happiness with a husband and father and must suffer his loss, Mary Knight stated that no changes in procedures were necessary and no disciplinary actions would be taken against any mental health official in this case. They covered everyone's ass and hid the facts by sealing all of the court records in this case.

Knight's hard-nosed and irresponsible attitude would allow her to continue to state, "The people with the responsibility for Bey's care carried through with that responsibility in an appropriate manner." Her cold, calloused attitude displayed insensitiveness to all concerned, and her super-ego and mismanagement was not corrected by her superiors. All of these facts only imprint more in everyone's minds that, "They don't care!" The only thing that matters is that the Westmont grounds must be vacated by the mentally ill to make room for land developers. These patients must be transferred or released in order for this to be achieved.

These last comments relate unconcern for the patient and community alike, and that the incompetent decisions being made by our state officials are resulting in chaos.

Statements were made by the psychiatric staffs at three separate institutions claiming that Bey should never be released. The system of unprofessional administrators ignored these statements by professionals and released patients regardless of their true state of mental health.

The court system and the state mental health system must be reviewed and changed, and they must be controlled by appropriate, competent, proficient, caring, professional individuals.

The state would save more money if they paid a decent salary to these professionals and, alternatively, the cost of law suits and tragedies would decrease, resulting in a lesser cost overall in the end. Think about it!

The House and Senate leaders of Pennsylvania outlined conflicting bills: one would force more people into institutions while the other would beef up outpatient programs.

"Derrick Smith Bey, mentally ill, who fatally stabbed a police officer, was new ammunition for involuntary commitments to state institutions. He had been in and out of hospitals for ten years and had severely beaten an attendant before being released into a group home."

The attendant was newly married and had small children to care for. His job was very important to him. Due to his injuries, he will never work again. His head was banged on the floor so hard and he was beaten so badly that it caused him to develop seizures and be hospitalized for a long period of time. He suffers from migraine headaches, weakness and experiences loss of balance. Even though he is receiving a disability pension, this does not replace his life as a father and active husband. The whole family will continue to suffer. This was not elaborated on in the press; they only said that he was injured by this patient.

"We can document case after case of the recidivists who have created a threat to society in general," said Senate Majority Leader Joseph Loeper, Jr. He also drafted mental health legislation for the 1985 shooting rampage by Sylvia Seegrist at the Springfield Mall. "This bill will prevent future violence by making it easier to commit people to a state hospital against their will. Seegrist had also been in and out of state institutions many times over the years. When her mother saw her behavior begin to escalate and tried to admit her, she was refused.

Under the current laws, a person cannot be committed for threats or property damage. There are too many Sylvia Seegrists and Derrick Smith Beys. People are killed on the streets by individuals who need to be in our mental health systems, and people living on the streets deserve better!

The well-intentioned "advocates" prompted deinstitutionalization, but thousands of released patients were let down by the system that was supposed to care for them once they were released. They are now found in subway tunnels, over steam vents, in cardboard boxes and in doorways."

Both bills are sincere attempts to better the health system that found the problems too complex. There will always be abuse and different interpretations of some sorts but both bills should have priorities and they are very different in their methods. They both want the best treatment for the mentally ill, and they both want society–as well as the patients themselves–protected.

Each case should be viewed on a personal basis, with examination of past history. Consideration of the safety of all concerned is the most important thing. Today patients are not kept locked up, as stated in The Quest and, with expert opinions from qualified specialists in the field of psychiatry, decisions should not fall under the same blanket for all!

As previously stated, "What works for some does not work for all." Schizophrenia is a very complex illness, and often a different method of treatment may be needed in individual cases. Some patients may respond to firmness, while others may become offended and lash back when a strict, structured environment is instituted: "They do not want to be told anything, they can hate the authoritative requests, etc."

A clear case of the onset of schizophrenia can be seen in the case histories in the past, and histories yet to unfold in the future may give you a better understanding of the normal-then-odd behavioral traits which could occur in someone's family.

Carol suffered from a nervous breakdown at the age of nineteen, forcing her to leave the trade school she was attending as she prepared for her future. She had always wanted to be a beautician, as she never excelled in academic subjects in school. She knew that she wasn't college material and wanted to become a success at something.

She was hospitalized for many months. She had a normal childhood, had the usual friends that children have and seemed to fit in anywhere. She never appeared to be nervous or depressed. She was medium build and had an unusually round face which glowed when she smiled. There was a twinkle in her eyes. Her hair was wavy and shimmered with golden highlights, and her eyes were the deepest blue.

Her school grades were average or below and studies came hard, but, with much hard work, she had always made the grade.

She seemed to suddenly drift away from her friends, spending more time in here room and becoming self-isolated. Her appetite was diminishing, and she kept aloof from the family. Her pleasant attitude started to display overtones of resentment and suspicion toward her friends and immediate family members. School became tedious and exasperating, and she started to miss classes and couldn't keep up with them. This caused frustration and anger and a feeling of incompetency that lead to low self-esteem.

It was not unusual for her parents to feel as if they were at fault: maybe they did not do something right; maybe they said the wrong things; maybe they were too strict; maybe it wasn't their fault; maybe there were too many pressures at school.

Carol's parents had reached their level of tolerance and thought that this was just a stage that she would grow out of. Should they just ignore this unusual behavior? Should they address the issue and demand explanations?

Finally Carol was taken to the family physician for examination and evaluation and, while there, she displayed hostile and paranoid traits. The doctor suggested that a psychiatrist see her for further evaluation and, with much persuasion, Carol was taken to a clinic and her history unfolded.

She remained there for several days and the dreaded diagnosis was revealed: "Schizophrenia, Paranoid Type!" This was unbelievable! How could this be? There was no history of mental illness in the family! What is schizophrenia? How long will it take for her to get better?

The doctor's answer was very vague, as there was no correct answer to give, only hope: "It may have a spontaneous remission," he stated, "but this only happens in about one-third of the cases."

This energetic, productive girl, whose young life was now in shambles, would become dependent on others to oversee her care and treatment. Her powers of concentration were diminishing and her attention span shortening. Carol was now experiencing hallucinations and responding to internal stimuli. She could be seen and heard talking to herself in a low, rapid tone and, at times, her attention could be redirected if her name was called.

After many months in the hospital, she was discharged to a group home but, shortly thereafter, was readmitted to the hospital. She was placed in a group home several times but, after the she eloped from the last one, and was seen downtown looking disheveled and dirty and eating from garbage cans, that she would again be readmitted to the hospital. Carol could not even remember some of the staff from the group home.

Carol was now considered a long termer in the state facility and was receiving care and treatment. She had remained there for fifteen years and was completely dependent on the staff for personal hygiene and appropriate attire. She had not responded to medications, but seemed to enjoy music and the recreation therapy groups. Carol was never problematic and always cooperated with staff.

Her parents were very supportive and showed interest in their daughter's welfare. They visited regularly and provided her with clothing and cigarettes. She became very receptive to these visits and was allowed to go home on short visits. She could not stay at home for long periods, though, as she would pace up and down and become irritable and argumentative.

Until some miraculous discovery in the field of psychiatry

would allow her to return home to the "norm," Carol will have to remain in a structured, protective and supervised environment.

The public has been exposed to the MRs (mentally retarded), autistic and dyslexic children on television programs. the news media has also endorsed them in a positive way. Sympathy for the mentally ill could emanate from such exposure but, if not relatively connected to these afflictions, no further interest is portrayed.

Mental illness was always portrayed in a negative manner when incidents or tragedies occurred. Just as the mentally retarded cannot help their behavior, neither can the mentally ill. The difference may be that mental disorders do not mean intellectually deficiency, as some of these people are highly intelligent but cannot control their behavior without support and medications.

Some MRs are housed in communities already and are functioning well with supervision. Their behaviors are usually predictable, and their idiosyncrasies usually never change. The difference with mental disorders is that their behaviors—and to what extent they may escalate—cannot always be predicted.

Patients who are interned and cared for by the same staff have a better chance of maintaining control. The staff knows the patients and their needs. They can respond to any unusual behavioral symptoms and know how to treat them. Sometimes a dose of P.R.N. medication is required. This is a dose of medicine given above the usual routine dose when periods of agitation occur. Patients will often ask for their P.R.N. dose when they begin to feel out of control, thus preventing harm to themselves or others.

Neighborhoods still protest against the MRs being replaced near to them. They are mostly fearful of their property being depreciated, and they do not teach their children tolerance toward the handicapped. They also do not want a large number of these homes in their neighborhoods. They feel that the staff monitoring these group homes are not really supervising all of them day and night. There are reports of parties and noises, and the neighbors feel that these homes are vulnerable and susceptible to crime. Many of these MR patients are functioning quite well and are taken to work daily and returned to the home. For some these homes can be a stepping stone to independence. If neighborhoods do not want the mentally retarded in their community, how do you think they would react to a group of hard-core mental patients?

The public is less fearful of the MRs and yet doesn't want

them. The old adage, "Not in my neighborhood," still rings true.

Most of Westmont's patients had no place to go, but society should demand that they deserve to be made comfortable and safe. Remember–in the beginning of this book we stated that many of the mentally ill who were originally instituted are now out of the hospital and functioning well in the community, as long as they continue their medications. We are only speaking here of the hard-core mentally ill!

One young man of twenty-nine years old already had a history of fifteen multiple, psychiatric hospitalizations. The precipitating factor of his illness appeared to be the death of his fourteen-year-old brother from a terminal illness when he was only ten years old. They had a close relationship and were constant companions. This was hard for him to handle and to understand. The two brothers were inseparable and were hardly seen without the other. They slept in the same room, ate the same meals, played the same games and went to church together each Sunday.

He was admitted for self-protection and the protection of others. Before his admissions, he had been treated for jumping in front of moving vehicles–because voices had told him to–on two different occasions. He had also jumped through a window and out of a moving car, took an overdose of valium, cut his wrists and would still state that he was no longer suicidal. He had a series of EST (Electric Shock Therapy), because he had previously requested restraints and, if not restrained upon his request, he would hurt staff and peers. Because he is overcome with undue anxiety, his family is fearful of his volatile and assaultive behavior and he can never go home again.

The parents visit regularly, supplying his needs of clothing, cigarettes and snacks. At times he is unreceptive and will evade them and, at other times, appears to tolerate their visits. The love and interest is seen in their faces and their reactions to their son. They never know what to expect when they come to visit. They also seem to understand his behaviors and his rejections. It is hopeful that someday advances in psychiatry will permit visitation once more in their family home. All avenues of treatment known to date have been tried on this young man.

Walter was a thirty-three-year-old man, an only child whose mother suffered from depression. He had a normal childhood and adolescence until the age of seventeen, when he became rebellious and verbally abusive to his parents. When they tried to discipline him or set the rules at home, he would defy them to the point of using profanity. It was clear that he had no respect for anyone. The parents were at the end of their wits, and wondered why he had suddenly changed. He started to wear dirty clothing to school for a week or more and he would sometimes sleep in them at night. He was smelly, dirty and unreasonable. His psychiatric status was becoming worse. He had held at least 100 jobs which lasted one or two days each.

Walter joined the Navy and was aboard an aircraft carrier for five months. He received a general discharge from the Navy fourteen months later. His parents did not wish him to return home to their house, so his dad rented him an apartment. When Walter found out, he became furious at his dad and threw a chair at him, causing multiple contusions on his arms and face. Afraid of his own son, the father ran from the apartment for fear of more injuries. At this time it appeared that Walter was really out of control. He had been verbally abusive before, but now he was physically abusive as well.

The parents now feared their son and had the locks changed on their doors to try and prevent him from entering. At first Walter did not go home, but other difficulties were surfacing. He began assaulting people on the streets for no apparent reason. He was arrested several time, but was always placed on probation. Walter was not yet diagnosed for his bizarre behaviors, and he was hallu-cinating, delusional by preoccupation of Hitler's death. The voices were occurring more often, but no one was aware of his suffering. He attempted to commit suicide on three different occasions: once by jumping out of a moving van, once by throwing himself in front of a moving vehicle, and once by cutting one wrist. He now was displaying hostile, aggressive, assaultive behaviors. He had no motivation, and his personal hygiene was bad and he appeared disheveled. He also had not shaved for quite some time and his hair was long, stringy and dirty. The landlord threw him out of the apartment, since the rent had not been paid for some time. Walter landed out on the streets until picked up by the police for display-ing the same hostile behavior described earlier. While in police custody, he was placed under observation. It was determined at that time that he was definitely suffering from a mental disorder. Admission to Westmont was his next step, where he was diagnosed and placed on medication. His behavior became more manage-able while medicated, and it appeared the activity group sessions were beneficial. He was never introverted and appeared to gain rapport with his peers as well as the staff. Walter's parents were notified of his admission but stated that they were afraid of him and, because of his numerous threats, did not want him home again.

Walter cannot hold an appropriate conversation, displays flight of ideas and a loss of thought content. He can relate to six or seven different topics in one paragraph. In other words, you could never interrogate him on any issue because one sentence would not correspond with the previous one. Occasionally, when out of control, Walter will need to be secluded and the medications do not always have the effect that they should. While instituted he will receive the attention and medication he requires. He will not comply with the medication routine and would probably forget to take his medicine. At least here, he will be protected from both society and himself.

Thirty-one-year-old Edwin Dougherty was a patient at Westmont for several years. After his parents were separated in 1957, his mother lived with another man. His father died in 1967 at the age of thirty-nine from cirrhosis of the liver. His childhood included argumentative parents and an alcoholic father. At the age of six years old, Edwin went to live with his grandmother, but he visited his mother frequently. Friends were scarce in his life, and he basically feared people. No doubt that, he suffered child abuse at the hands of a drunken father.

Ed was a good student, but would cry a lot and was moved frequently from school to school. He never participated in sports at school and kept more or less to himself. Although he reached the twelfth grade, he dropped out of school just before.

He had a history of sniffing glue at the age of thirteen with a group of teenagers, which only lead to more self-isolation and withdrawal. His mother took him to see a psychiatrist and was under his care from the age of fourteen to sixteen, but was told that he was a "normal boy" by the doctor.

There is a brief work history of dishwashing in a restaurant, as well as work for a furniture mover because he was tall, big and strong. These are the only two jobs on record. He has not worked since and never married or sired children.

He was hospitalized in 1981 for a short period of time before being discharged to his mother's care. While at home, he became very nervous and smoked constantly, talked to himself and would occasionally sniff ignition spray.

He was picked up by the police for masturbating on a bus

and was returned home. His mother took him to PATH, who assisted her in getting him committed. His mood became tense, restless, hostile and angry, and his new behavior included uncontrollable screaming on the streets.

Edwin is still a patient under hospital care. He responds to internal stimuli and appears preoccupied with hallucinations and delusions which cause an inability to function. He is unconcerned about his appearance and needs supervision and direction in everyday living skills. His history of screaming and shouting in public caused hospitalization at least one-half dozen times–he progressively got worse and shouting spells became longer in duration. He could be seen biting his arm, shadow boxing on the walls, talking to himself and frightening people. Upon the death of his grandfather, he became more violent and destructive at home and displayed uncontrollable behavior such as punching the walls and breaking furniture.

Today his family will take him home for short visits but will never let him live there again. If you saw Edwin walking down the street and, if he was not shouting or screaming, he would appear perfectly normal. He is a good-looking man and he walks with a normal stride. But even with his medication, he can become uncontrollable and need a dose of P.R.N. to calm his anxieties.

John was a medium-built man who was frail looking and disheveled in appearance. He had to be reminded to shave and shower and showed no interest in his appearance. He was usually cooperative with the staff, and also seemed to choose his peers for friends. He was in his early thirties and had been a patient for at least twelve years. He was being considered for community placement by the assessor who received his chart. He still had delusions that he was a psychiatrist and a doctor, and that he was controlled by a computer. He also thought that the television was speaking directly to him. He was also preoccupied with religion. Withdrawal from reality and self-isolation were symptoms he often displayed.

John was a chronic eloper and, if given the chance, would just take off. He never complied with aftercare when he was previously released to a half-way house and even eloped form there. His mother died at the age of fifty from Hodgkin's Disease. She was a professor of art and had been employed at one of the state's colleges.

John's father died at the age of forty from lung cancer. The mother remarried and John's stepfather physically and sexually abused him. John lived in a constant state of anxiety and fear of what his stepfather would do next. He was placed in a boarding school at the age of thirteen after his mother died, and his stepfather was denied custody.

John then lived with his sister until graduation from high school. His problems only grew from there. He attended Pierce Junior College, where he accused others of being gay. He never completed college and started working during the summer painting houses. He began displaying paranoid traits and was forced to leave this job. Other odd jobs were also not kept very long because he made mistakes and was slow in performance. He began talking to himself. He was admitted to a general hospital for a period of two weeks, but was discharged because of his refusal to comply with medications. John tried to receive treatment at his community health center, but he again became lax with routine medication. He later was again admitted to a Lancaster general hospital and from there was discharged to a half-way house. Because he became preoccupied with religion, started disrobing in the streets, was not eating, and suffered from insomnia and agitation, he was admitted to another psychiatric facility.

While there he talked about nothing but death or hurting himself. Other behaviors surfaced, and he became assaultive and knocked his friend to the floor, kicking him in the ribs–fracturing several–and had to be admitted to a general hospital for treatment. When this incident occurred, he was transferred to Westmont. After two years, he complied with his medication routine and it is believed that he tricked the therapists into believing that he would comply with outside treatment. He was then discharged through the courts, and his whereabouts are not known at this time. We believe that, due to his past history with noncompliance, it would be amazing if he had followed through.

Carl Danton was diagnosed with paranoid schizophrenia and was sent to Rothman Center for evaluation. He was known to display unpredictable behavior, with potential assaultiveness as one of the known symptoms. He as easily distracted when responding to internal stimuli–such as hearing imagined voices–and could be communicated with if verbal intervention was used. When Carl was talking to himself and a staff member would say, "Carl, come here. I want you to take your shower now," he should say, "Alright. Be right there." He would then get his clean clothing out and proceed to the shower. If nothing was said to him, he would continue to talk to himself and be unaware of his environment. Verbal intervention did not always work and thus require a P.R.N. medication to suppress this symptom. He would often threaten self-abuse if discharge from Westmont was mentioned, and he had a history of eloping.

Carl was a constant threat to his family, and they were fearful that he may locate them. His grooming, as well as his personal appearance and hygiene, was poor unless directed by the staff. He required help using the toilet at night. He showed agitation by talking to himself and laughing inappropriately and pacing around the ward, holding his hand over his blind left eye. He believed that the reflection in the mirror was talking to him. There was also a history of suicide attempts. The family felt intimidated by him. His sister always ignored him and told everyone that she couldn't stand him.

His younger brother felt sorry for him. Although the brother loved him, he said he could not live with him. As a small child, Carl would destroy or climb out of the crib or playpen. At the age of fourteen he was already using street drugs and hung around with gangs. He was never able to sustain himself in communities. His parents refused to let him live at home.

He was arrested twice for possession of marijuana. He was also arrested at the ages of fifteen and seventeen for assault and battery and was placed on probation. Carl was placed with a family in Bucks County but eloped soon after. He was taken to a state institution at the age of sixteen, where he was then released home, became reclusive and did not want to leave the house. His parents were willing to try again, even though they had said he could not come home.

When this behavior was noted, his parents took him to another facility for treatment. While there he became worse by displaying threatening and destructive symptoms. The juvenile authorities arrested him again and placed him into yet another Northwest institution, only for him to be released again to his home.

While there he shot himself in the face with a shotgun, causing extensive damage to his face and resulting in the loss of his left eye. Reconstructive surgery began, and he required three operations. After his release from the hospital, he again began using street drugs and this time threw himself in front of a truck, which caused him to be admitted to another state hospital before transfer to Westmont.

The family suffered emotionally, physiologically, financially and physically as a result of this patient's drug abuse and subsequent, resultant psychiatric problems.

Another patient who was sent to Rothman Center to be reevaluated was Norman Falk, who had a long history of psychiatric hospitalizations and prison incarcerations by the age of twenty-eight. There was also a long history of drug abuse recorded since the age of twelve. It is not known why he turned to drugs at such an early age. There could have been some peer pressure from his childhood friends, or perhaps drugs were very accessible in his school. He started stealing money from his mother's pocketbook, and there were also articles missing from the house. It is believed that he stole them to support his drug habit. This precipitated his crime wave of burglaries, which resulted in the numerous arrests that followed.

He refused to believe that he had a problem and would thus never seek and help. He seemed quite content to serve out several sentences, and, when he was returned to society, he continued in the same manner until other behavior patterns started to manifest, including aggressive, assaultive behavior. His behavior resulted in injuries to one man, who was admitted to a metropolitan hospital with af fractured arm and two broken ribs. Again Norman was arrested and served a few months until he assaulted one guard and spit on several others.

It was felt by the courts that this man needed to have a psychiatric evaluation; it was determined that he suffered from a mental disorder and was sent to Westmont. Norman was not always cooperative with ward routines and believed that the medication given to him was poison. His aggressive behavior eventually subsided, and he was more in control when he would continue with his medications.

He received ground privileges and handled them very well, returning to the building for meals and the census check. Only occasionally would there be a confrontation with one of his peers, and this was usually over cigarettes. Occasionally he was caught rooting through lockers and drawers of other patients looking for money, cigarettes or snacks. He could not be trusted on the ward when out of sight because of his thievery. His mother never came to visit him and did not want him to return home. The only support he received was from the staff; no one else held any interest in his welfare.

The following is an example of the incidents that occurred in the city after the discharge of mental patients who were out in the community. This appeared in The Quest, only because the facts would be hard to hide as the public was already witness it it.

"A woman was pushed from a subway platform" into the path of a train, by a man who told the police that he was responding to a voice command. The fifty-six year old Mrs. Warrington was grabbed by the shoulders and hurled from the platform. Horrified onlookers saw several cars pass over her, but she did not die. She was rushed to a nearly hospital in critical condition, sustaining fractures of the legs, pelvis and skull.

The man, Edward Jones, a discharged patient from Westmont, was seen bobbing his head up and down and looking at this woman before the train arrived. A witness stated that as the train approached, everyone walked to the edge of the platform; as the train started to pass them, the man grabbed the lady by the shoulders and shoved her off the platform, over the edge.

Jones started to run away but was wrestled to the ground by a witness who was an ex-wrestler. As police came and escorted him away, you could hear him saying that the voices had told him to do it!

Now pay attention to this: The charges by the police were aggravated assault and simple assault, recklessly endangering another person and risking a catastrophy! This article was written by Tom Gibbons of The Quest.

In September, 1989, at the trial of Edward Jones, the prosecutor termed the incident an "unspeakable horror." He was in agreement with the defense lawyer, who contended that Jones was mentally ill, with severe paranoid schizophrenia, and had "no criminal intent" when he pushed Mrs. Warrington from the train platform.

In Jones's mind, he was responding to internal stimuli that told him that the woman had a demon inside of her, and the demon visualized the rape of all black women. The issue of the case was the mental condition of the patient.

Mrs. Warrington, who worked in a nursing home, stated, "He's not all that crazy, and he messed up my life. I can't work! I can't drive! I can't do anything I want!" She hobbled to the witness stand with the aid of a walker, her right leg suspended in a brace. She had suffered three broken ribs, a broken back and was confined to a body brace for many months. Mrs. Warrington also related that she now wore dentures because her teeth were knocked out and ended up in her stomach.

Mr. Jones had been hospitalized "dozens of times," but had periods of remission. He had been hospitalized three times in eight months prior to this incident, but was released into the community in October, 1988. His delusions and hallucinations continued, and his mother had attempted to have him committed before this incident occurred.

In mid-September, the trial was over and the verdict was in. Mr. Jones would be confined in a jail–instead of a mental institution–for a period of ten to twelve years. If, at that time, he still portrayed psychiatric symptoms, he would then be incarcerated in a state forensic unit.

This incident would never have happened if Mr. Jones had not been released into the community. And he did not belong in a jail! He should have been returned to a mental facility to receive treatment instead of being incarcerated in a jail. The judicial decisions must be more responsible to both the patients and communities!

Bruce Wilson was a poor black man about forty years of age. He was of medium height, had a stocky build, and walked with a fast shuffle. He was very concerned when it came to his mother. He had never known his father and worried about his mother working so hard to carve out an existence. Being the oldest, he felt an obligation to quit school at the age of fifteen to help support his family of three brothers and two sisters. He had worked as a shoe shine boy until the age of twelve. Bruce worked odd jobs of all sorts until he was drafted into the Army. He served in Korea and Japan for a brief period of sixteen months, and received an honorable discharge due to "nerve problems." Besides receiving V.A. benefits, he sold his blood twice weekly. He was married and divorced twice, and a daughter resulted from the second marriage.

Bruce was arrested and convicted for possession of an unlicensed gun and was given a two year probation. It was believed that he committed arson and burglary at a former residence. Bruce dealt with the problems in his first marriage by drinking excessively, and this is when he began hearing voices. Bruce was admitted for brief periods in several different hospitals. Problems arose when he refused to comply with out-patient programs.

Due to his history of mental illness and alcohol abuse, he suffers from some sensory impairment. Bruce's daughter never responded to contacts from him, nor did she ever come to visit him.

Leo bush had always resented authority and was very belligerent as a child. His mother thought that his behavior was bizarre at times. He was always hard to control. She thought that he could be considered a "wild child," always very hyperactive and getting into fights. He seemed to have a low frustration level and was very argumentative. This patient was about five-foot-three inches tall but was obese and thus very strong. Yes! He could be feared when motivated to anger.

At seventeen years of age, he stabbed a man who died due to complications. He was arrested and sent to a forensic unit in a state facility for this act. While there he regressed and was admitted to a general hospital for treatment. Leo was not allowed to return home due to his belligerent and threatening attitude toward his mother. He was grossly disorganized, delusional, confused and disoriented. His speech was incoherent. He would claim, "I'm dead," "I'm sterile," since he had no children.

While in the community as an out-patient, he had poor follow-through with his medication routine. He was considered incompetent and had a tendency to give away money. At the time, he was withdrawn, had deteriorated personal hygiene and seldom took baths. When at home, he would leave without closing the doors and would take his pants off in the middle of the street. He was considered a threat to self and others due to his outbursts of hostility, assaultiveness, agitation and threatening behavior.

Elliot Townsend had a history of sexual deviancy and assaultiveness and was admitted to Westmont from a detention center several years previously after raping a young neighborhood boy. Elliot had a long history of institution living. He was interned at a mental retardation facility for a period of seven years. He was known as a duel diagnosis, having MR as well as schizophrenia.

From the MR facility, he was discharged to live with his sister. Because of aggressive behavior, he again was readmitted to the MR unit. While there he attacked another patient and beat him severely for refusing to have sex with him. Because of this incident, he was transferred to a state mental hospital from where he again was discharged into the custody of his sister.

While at his sister's home, he beat her when she rebuffed his attempts to have sex with her. He was sent by the police to a general hospital, and was then transferred to Westmont. Elliot was again discharged after four months; upon release he attempted to rape his young niece. He was readmitted to Westmont once more and stated that voices told him to "rape girls."

The few cases discussed in this chapter will give you a clear understanding of "hard-core" or "terminally ill" mental patients. These patients need constant supervision and a structured environment. These are the patients who cannot return to society. Communities, as well as the patients who have been given these opportunities to function in the community, must be protected.

Unknown to the residents of Philadelphia, the state was purchasing and leasing properties throughout the communities in order to place mental patients into these areas. This was the part of their placement program known as "independent housing."

The communities were uninformed and unaware of the plan to place mental patients into their neighborhoods as residents. The landlords leasing these properties to the state had not attempted to gain the approval of the neighbors.

As stated previously, the public does not want the CLA (Community Living Arrangement) housing, which houses several mentally retarded patients who may be educable and productive, next door to them. The mentally retarded are different than the mentally ill, and yet you often hear them included in the same breath.

The remaining patients residing in Westmont were the hard-core patients, and these were the people that the state was placing into the communities.

A house was leased in the Southwest section of Philadelphia in which the state placed two male patients among unsuspecting residents. There were two male counselors assigned to stay with them. The commotion created by these patients in the house caused an uprising amidst the residents of that area, and before a volatile situation could arise, the state removed the patients and transported them to a cabin in the Pocono Mountains. The two male patients, Jim and Joe, were accompanied by the two counselors who would stay with them.

An article related to this occurrence in the city's newspapers stated: "To cushion the patients' disappointment, they were sent to the Poconos with two counselors for a week. They stayed in a cabin that the state had leased for use by patients with staff during the closing. The two young men enjoyed a week of fishing and boating, then returned to live in one of the assessment facilities until permanent housing was available."

This news item was dictated by Ethel Richter, for public consumption relating a beautiful story of the state's concern for clients. After reading this story, the public would certainly feel as if the state cared about the mental patients from Westmont.

This explained to the press and public that the state would remedy any occurrence which involved these clients in a positive way.

The reporter did not investigate this incident, but took Richter at her word. The true events will now be told!

This will prove the manipulative steps taken to gain the consensus of the public. Can you believe anything that you read in the press? You will see for yourself how helpful the media is and how it can sway minds, in this case, to accept the closing of Westmont.

It was early in the week, and night had fallen. One of the staff members awoke in the early morning hours and proceeded to check on his clients. Jim, one of the clients, was awake and lying on his back in bed with his eyes staring toward the ceiling. As the staff member approached, Jim's eyes rolled downward and glanced at him.

"Where's Joe? I don't see him," the staff person said in a questioning manner.

"I don't know," Jim said unconcerned.

After searching the cabin and not being able to find Joe, the staff member decided to hunt for him outside. The other staff person still lay sleeping and was not aroused by his presence.

"Let's look outside, Jim! Come on! Come with me!"

The two men departed into the dense, dark woods surrounding the cabin, crumpling the twigs beneath their shoes, creating small crackling noises as they walked away. Suddenly, one foot and then the other tripped into a hole in the ground which was not visible due to the spread of leaves. The staff member discovered that the hole was too deep to escape from without help.

"Jim, go get the other counselor to help me out!"

Soon the two men returned and rescued the counselor from the pit. He brushed the leaves from his clothing and stamped his feet to see if they were alright. The three proceeded towards the cabin, only to see Joe standing inside, clutching a dirty, rusty hatchet in his right hand. You could tell by the rotted wooden handle and the rust crusted blade that this tool must have been laying around unused for many months.

"Why did you leave the cabin Joe?" asked one of the staff members.

"I wanted to get some air, and I wanted to smoke a cigarette!"

"Where did you get the hatchet that you have in your hand?"

"I found it in the woods!"

"Give it to me please," begged the staff member in a firm but calm voice.

You could see the anger building up on Joe's face. Joe's eyes were squinting when he dropped the hatchet to the floor; he then reeled around and grabbed a kitchen knife that was lying on the drainboard of the sink.

The two staff members lunged forward in an attempt to disarm Joe and retrieve the knife. The commotion and struggling aroused the neighbors, and during this excitement, someone had called the police. The neighbors were angry and upset, as they were not used to incidents such as these in their community. This had been a quiet and serene retreat for them, a place to enjoy the outdoors. This excitement was new to them!

When the police arrived, they almost arrested one of the staff in the confusion. The two male clients were removed by the state and returned to Rothman Center, where Jim remained; Joe, however, was sent to Bordentown State Hospital with a change in his commitment from voluntary to a 302–involuntary–and there he would remain.

Now you can compare these two stories, the true one and the one issued to the press.

"CITY AND STATE CLASH OVER FUNDS WHICH ARE BLOCKING THE EXIT OF PATIENTS," read a headline in The Quest. The target closure date of September 30 seemed unlikely due to the conflict between the officials over housing. Closing the hospital proved to be a massive undertaking. The lawyers for the families filed a law suit on behalf of the patients before the September date.

Knight's statements only prove what has been said all along in this novel, that these patients are considered to be bodies, to be transferred like cattle to a farm somewhere. The hell with the patients!——The hell with the families!——The hell with the staff!

Ethel Richter was quoted in the newspaper stating there were two cases that she could name off hand where the patents had benefitted through placement planning: one patient no longer wet the bed; the other patient, who had never worn shoes before, now wore them.

Did she ever mention the suicides and deaths which were caused by the placement program?

Ronald was a medium built man of average height who appeared to be quite content residing at Westmont. His diagnosis was paranoid schizophrenia, and he entertained thoughts of suicide. He was fairly cooperative with staff members and mingled intermittently with his peers. He was discharged from the hospital.

While on the grounds of the hospital, he had befriended another patient name Melissa and displayed affection for her. After his discharge, he would appear on the grounds and the two of them were seen together frequently. They communicated by telephone, and it appeared that they had a continuing relationship.

Ronald was often seen attired in female clothing, including beads and a pocketbook. He would dress according to his mood swing.

One evening the television news stated that a woman had jumped in front of a subway train and was killed. The picture viewed by the audience was that of two policemen carrying a litter up a pair of stairs, and the body was covered with a sheet.

The coroner's office was amazed to discover a male body under the woman's clothing. It was disclosed later that this had been Ronald. He had finally accomplished what he had threatened many times to do.

There was no indication in the press that anyone from Westmont had been killed. The news coverage was brief on the first day and was never mentioned again.

Marion was almost forty years old, with a birthday around the corner. She had been at Westmont for eleven years and was admitted here for tossing her seven-year-old son out of a window, which resulted in his death. She had drowned her first son at the tender age of three in a bathtub.

Her mother was Jewish and her father was a black man. She was a beautiful woman with dark, shiny hair, which had a natural wave and was always combed just so. Her complexion was light and flawless, and her make up was always nicely worn. She always seemed normal to the staff, and she could converse sensibly. She washed her own clothing and dressed neatly all of the time.

Marion never wore dresses, but her blue jeans were always clean and neat. She was one of the patients who always took pride in her appearance.

She was committed to Westmont by the courts, and sanity hearings were held intermittently. She harbored a fear that if the hospital closed, she would have to return to jail. The thought of closure frightened her more than anyone realized.

Marion was housed on a coed ward, where she became fond of a male patient who would later be discharged. He came to see her regularly, and it was believed that she expressed hopes of marrying this man sometime in the future.

The week before her suicide, Marion had another court date. The decision was reached in court for her to remain court committed for a longer period of time. As talk of closure in one form or another was almost daily, she silently knew that her blanket of security would soon be gone. She had felt safe at Westmont, and the thought of leaving may have contributed to her suicide.

The week before her fate, she remained calm and cooperative, and the staff was unaware of her future intentions. Yes! The fear of ineligibility for community placement when the hospital closed was constantly on her mind, but no one knew!

No one guessed that she was contemplating her own death. Who could tell? She did not appear depressed, nervous or anxious. She had hidden her most inner thoughts and had played a role for the unsuspecting staff. She was clever enough to handle her ground privileges, and always returned to the ward for her meals and the taking of the census.

One bright Sunday afternoon, she returned as usual to the ward for her medications, then requested to return to grounds. When dinner time arrived, she did not return to the ward. This was unusual, and the staff became apprehensive and started to search the grounds for her. One patient said that she was seen getting into a blue van, but this could not be substantiated.

It wasn't until a phone call was received that evening from the New York police that everyone would learn her fate. She had somehow gotten a ride to New York and decided there that she no longer wished to live. She had shown unusual interest in the death of Ronald and had been seen talking to his friend, Melissa, right after the incident.

The phone call from the New York police revealed how

Marion committed suicide. She had jumped in front of an oncoming train in the subway station and was killed instantly. This was one week after Ronald had done the same thing in the same way! Perhaps she was carrying this thought around for the week since Ronald's death, and the idea of a quick death may have appealed to her at the time.

Perhaps society contributed to Marion's entire existence through the repeated rejections of her and of her children. Who knows what torments she imagined and the paranoid expressions of futility due to her mixed racial heritage. Although she felt more accepted in the black community, there must have been some rejection from both.

Marion was not formally identified for two and one-half weeks. Why so long? Had she not been a court commitment? Were here fingerprints not on file? Why struggle with dental records when a positive identification could have been done instantly? The only way she was immediately identified on the scene was by a picture badge from Westmont which was still in her handbag. There was never mention of this incident on the television or in the press. That would have adversely affected the order to close Westmont!

Marion's death would not come to light in the media until October, four months later. Because Marion had ground privileges, the judge tried to wiggle out of her responsibility for this death by stating that, "She should have been supervised." Yet the judge had allowed ground privileges five years earlier! The judge now stated that she should have been outside in an enclosed area. This statement placed the blame on the psychiatrist who had written for the ground privilege.

Condemnations and excuses flowed like wine, with everyone trying to shift the blame to the next guy. Mr. Tweedil explained that Marion seemed depressed in the recent months due to the notice of the hospital closing. He also stated that she had many friends who were discharged from the hospital into the community and also wanted to be free. Why, then, did he not relate this information to the staff? Mr. Tweedil thought that he was a professional because he was a consumer advocate, and yet he did not understand the complexities of schizophrenia or the importance of the relative information he thought he had.

Everyone offered excuses to desensitize their own feelings of guilt, and yet this incident could not have been predicted. We are dealing with the human mind, and although you may think that you know the answers to a patient's problems, you could be wrong. If every suicidal incident was predictable, our statistics would be lower. How many people will state that they had no idea a person was suicidal: "They seemed so happy, they had everything going for them." etc.

Is there no doubt now that a "gag" was placed on the media to not disclose the impending incidents concerning the patients from Westmont?

Investigations were held–hush-hush as administrators tried to find some logical reasoning for this happening. Who was to blame?

The entire State Mental Health System was the answer, for contributing to the frustrations and anxieties among the patients. As stated previously, mental patients are not stupid–some are highly intelligent. Their thinking may be twisted at times, but, overall, they can understand certain situations better than others.

Other cases have also been listed in this book as to the incidents and events that occurred due to the "Bold Plan of Community Placement."

Suicide is a general term, and yet the reasoning behind it is not fully understood. Suicide can be a result of a mental disorder, although many environmental and social encounters may be contributors. Thoughts of suicide can progressively lead to death.

First there is the idea of suicide–a loss of the desire to live–but no injury had yet come about. then there are attempted suicides that may not result in death, only physical injury. A completed suicide results in death.

There are a recorded 20,000 completed suicides in the United States annually, and it is the tenth leading cause of death among adults and among one-third of youths. Teenage suicides have tripled in the past decade, and it is highest among white males.

In attempted suicides, females under thirty out number males. First time suicide attempts have a high risk for repeat in the first year following the initial act.

Males choose mostly from explosives or firearms, while females choose from poisoning or sleeping pills. Attempts at wrist slashing are common among both sexes, while throat slashing occurs predominately among males. Women choose the milder form of suicidal actions, where males are more violent. Females are less successful than males, which may account for the higher incidents recorded in the male population. Lately the trend has increased to jumping in front of, or out of, moving vehicles.

Suicides are usually associated with social stigma. The public's attitude regarding suicide is that it is a crime. In 1961, England repealed the law that made it a crime. Canada followed suit in 1972. In the United States, attempted suicide is still a crime in nine states. "Libertarians" argue that an individual has a right to take his or her own life.

A current trend includes studying a broader complex of "life threatening" or "risk taking" behaviors, which may diminish the stigma and turn people toward helping the individual who sees suicide as the only answer to their problems. Suicides associated with stigma are:

1) unsolved psychic conflict
2) defects in personality
3) environmental pressures, economic or social upheavals, or changes in one's socioeconomic status
4) an expression of feelings or a "cry for help"
5) job loss or bereavements
6) chronic physical illness
7) psychotic disturbances, drug or alcohol abuse
8) low self-esteem
9) feeling of confusion or despondency
10) feeling of hopelessness, a negative future, like nothing can be done
11) break-up of the family unit, divorce or separation

Today, in practically every city, hot lines are set up for the prevention of suicides. there is usually a 24 hour emergency community health center with dedicated staff and ongoing programs. Most colleges and schools have a crisis center, with professional psychologists on staff to prevent such suicides.

The radio talk shows, especially in the early morning hours, have responded sympathetically when callers call to relay their intentions.

The psychological researchers are focusing on the phenomena of attempted and completed suicides. Mortality rates in society, per 100,000 population, reveal that white males predominate throughout the age categories, except from ages 25-34. As white males age, the incidents increase in the group of completed suicides. The following figures were adapted from the United States Bureau of Census 1975, "Statistical Abstract of the United States," pages 154-155:

Ages	White Males	Black Males	White Females	Black Females
5-14	0.7%	0.3%	0.2%	0.1%
15-24	17.4%	14.0%	4.3%	4.1%
25-34	21.8%	22.6%	8.5%	5.3%
35-44	22.8%	14.3%	12.2%	5.4%
45-54	28.4%	3.4%	13.7%	3.2%
55-64	32.4%	12.1%	12.0%	4.4%
65 & over	40.7%	11.9%	8.2%	3.1%

The preceding information denotes that the rate of black female suicides is the lowest statistically. Females are less likely to complete suicide attempts than are males. This strange phenomena remains a puzzling reality, with many questions unanswered:

1) Could it be the pressures of society and the economic standards set forth by the communities and the media?
2) Could it be part of the contributing factors that result in the decrease of stability in the family unit?
3) Could it be a product of one-parent families or a lack of confidentiality and love from a life-time partner in a marriage?
4) Could it be man's self-worth declining because of the liberation movement of women's organizations that downgrade the male role in this country?
5) Could the sex revolution be attributed to the infidelity among married couples?

The questions go on and one, but no one seems to have the answers. It appears that society has contributed after all to the downgrading of the male role and the white male particularly.

Men have always struggled playing the leading "macho" role in a family unit, caring for his wife and providing for his family in general. Fathers used to be the primary disciplinarian in the family, was respected by his wife, children and the community, and was considered the head of the house, "king of the castle."

Today's established society sets forth economic standards which, in many cases, necessitates two parents working to maintain their image in the community and the equalization of their children with their peers.

The monetary pressures placed on the male and the feeling of "keeping his head above water" can be overbearing. He must fulfill the expectations of his family! These types of pressures can lead to depression, a feeling of being overwhelmed, problems with finances and a twisted sense of direction.

Often these factors contribute to the abuses of alcohol and drugs as a means of escape from these pressures. All or some of these combined factors are responsible for a great number of suicides in this country. Dependence becomes an issue to deal with.

Heavy drinking over a long period of time can result in mental disorders or permanent brain and nervous system damage. Drug abuse can precipitate hallucinatory and erratic behaviors, which may possibly include schizophrenic traits. Alcohol and drugs may lead to loss of job, and a stable family life, law violations (thefts, burglary or prostitution), loss of personal property, loss of family contact and a deep sense of despair.

Drug abuse effects the thinking process and may produce changes in mood or behavior, which in turn can lead to physical and psychological dependence.

Drug abuse may emanate from curiosity or a need for instant relief from individual problems. There are three major groups of drugs known to users: uppers (stimulants), downers (depressants) and hallucinogens (LSD).

In Wilmington, Delaware, around noon on a Sunday afternoon, a five-year-old girl walked into the bathroom, and discovered her mother in the process of attempting suicide by slitting her wrists. Angry at this intrusion, the mother turned around and stabbed her daughter thirty times with two six-inch steak knives, puncturing both of the girl's lungs.

The paramedics rushed the child to the nearest hospital, where she was admitted directly to surgery. She was in serious condition, with multiple knife wounds to her chest, back and arms.

When asked by the police, "Why did you do this to your daughter?" the mother replied, "I had to. The Devil made me do it!" The mother was arrested and taken to jail. While there she broke the glass out of the door of the holding cell, and was then taken to a state mental institution for evaluation.

Are there any public statistics categorizing numbers of the mentally ill who completed suicides, or are they included in the total sum when these numbers are compiled?

Threats of suicide are not to be taken lightly. Depressed people may also entertain thoughts of suicide, but, once when spoken of, the meaning and intent become more real.

Two recent cases of lawsuits against the state concerning mentally ill relatives only endorse the reality of the verbal threats that lead to two completed suicides. Both men had purchased guns, and both men inflicted their own deaths.

Are psychiatrists capable of predicting violence, especially with the inadequacy of today's existing out-patient care?

One patient had a history of elopement from the hospital, and it was stated that the position of the doctor was to release the patient, as he "would run away anyhow!" Three months after his release, he killed himself with a rifle. His last admittance to the hospital was due to the fact that he had purchased a gun and threatened suicide. While at home on a day pass, his family had to wrestle a gun away from him.

This man had a history of thirty-nine hospitalizations, and was only twenty-eight years old. He had not believed that he was mentally ill, and thus did not comply with his medication routine. This patient was not only diagnosed as a manic depressive (also known as Bi-Polar Disorder), but he was a known alcoholic abuser, which made his release questionable in the first place.

The other man was thirty-six years old and not only took his own life, but that of his six-year-old son as well. The hospital would not commit him as an involuntary patient in spite of his suicidal threats, which made him more vulnerable to release and discharge.

It was only seventeen days after his release that he accomplished his suicide and the death of his son who he had kidnapped from a school bus at the end of the school day.

Ten days before his release, he had been given unsupervised ground privileges, regardless of his defiance of the medication routine, volunteer absence from group therapy and a continuation of suicide threats.

Here was a man who had tried but could not cope with reality and, in his own way, was begging for help. In both of these cases, the schizophrenic traits and bizarre behaviors had surfaced in their late teens or early twenties. Once again these traits were not immediately diagnosed, and were considered "normal" but angry behaviors. They also complicated their illnesses with the abuse of alcohol and, possible, drugs. In both cases, the men did not believe that they were mentally ill.

At first their behaviors were accepted as a maladjustment or anxiety over their own situations at the time. They both became progressively worse, and their symptoms and suicidal ideas appeared to be forgotten when they were in remission.

Professionals are still groping at straws for some positive, concrete method of treating the mentally ill. Although it seems that a bill of rights for the patients would be a necessary component of their treatment plan, to also have this bill can also be abused within the good intentions of these professionals. The laws must be made clear, and the protection of psychiatric treatment must also be upheld. Patient's rights must not supersede patient's safety. A clearer meaning should be invoked so as to not interfere with good patient treatment and protection.

Deinstitutionalization has allowed desperately ill street people who simply don't want treatment or shy away from it. In a courtroom battle in the New York Manhattan district, Joyce Brown, alias "Billie Boggs," was hospitalized by Mayor Koch against her will. She shouted at passers-by, tore up dollar bills, urinated and defecated on the sidewalks and street, but a trial judge pronounced her "sane."

"We have condemned the homeless mentally ill to die with their rights on," protested Charles Krauthammer, a columnist.

As it stands now, lawyers, not doctors, decide when someone should be hospitalized.

Late in July, 1989, another article appeared in the newspaper relating again to their most used word–and the only terminology known to them when it came to Westmont–"ABUSE." Drastic increase in the potential for remaining patients to be ABUSED, due to the loss of qualified staff; there was concern that Westmont was a ticking time bomb situation, with declining quality of patient care and the increase for all forms of ABUSE. The Quest tried–and partially succeeded in some cases–to produce anxieties for the families of patients. Also stated was the fact that the hospital nurses were provided by temporary employment agencies, weren't familiar with the patients and other staff members and could not provide continuity of care.

They did not know that ten or more of these agency nurses were previously employed at Westmont, many of them in a supervisory position. They had an average of fifteen to twenty-five years of service, and knew the patients, hospital policies and the staff very well.

The paper also stated that the staff was too tired to be one hundred percent alert and effective because of the demands of overtime. The staff knew their limits and would refuse shifts if too tired!

Let The Quest also explore the overtime status at hospitals in the rest of the communities and see if they are any different!

Soon after this article appeared in the press, Mary Knight became upset at the information being released to the press and, the following week, transferred the acting superintendent to another state hospital, with a lesser position and a great salary cut. Those rising to the top in government can be easily toppled!

The top echelon of the hospital said their farewells to the superintendent and took him out to lunch on a Friday. He was sad when he left, and good wishes were conveyed by his peers in the administration.

Who would be the superintendent now? Everyone wondered who was in charge. It didn't take too long to find out. On the following Monday, the superintendent was back! What happened??

It seemed that Mary Knight had exceeded her powers by not consulting with her boss, Mr. Whitman! Her egotistical, energetic, overbearing sense of power made her forget the chain of command and forget to consult with Whitman regarding the demotion and removal of the hospital superintendent. When Whitman learned of her action of removal, he quickly brought him back to Westmont. Whitman had already fired one superintendent and did not want to be credited with two such firings. This would be too much to explain to both his superiors and the public. After all The Quest had related some truth in that article, especially that the state had transferred off experienced staff and had hired people who had never come in contact with this type of patient before.

On Tuesday of the same week, the superintendent was seen on the wards, asking whether the patients had been outside on this lovely, clear day. He must have been told to make himself visible, as if he really cared about the patients.

Mr. Whitman needed him to take the brunt of any situation which might arise and need answers. A hospital without a superintendent would not be able to blame any particular person for its fumbling. Yes! The superintendent must be in place!

After Derrick Smith Bey killed a Septa police officer at a bus terminal last spring, the papers reported that Bey had been released from a state hospital, even though he was notoriously violent there. Knight said he'd been handled correctly. Who's crazy here?

The news media would state that the patients were at risk because of the inexperienced staff at the hospital, but this was soon questioned by the communities. Shortly after the article appeared claiming the risk factor, a woman wrote her story to the newspaper. She said that as she was walking along a street in the middle of downtown, a street person who was making his home on the sidewalk suddenly lunged toward her. He slapped her and attempted to push her into the street, in front of the path of oncoming cars. He failed, and she summoned a policeman who merely chased him down the street to another spot. The policeman said, "With Westmont closing, there will probably be an increase in such incidents. No wonder people are moving away from the city!" The woman asked herself, "Who's at risk?"

Situations like these were becoming more frequent but were not being publicized. Mary Knight had stated that the discharged patients were always being followed-up and that she knew where every one was. When placing the chronic mental patients in the community, they were somehow ending up in the streets.

In Whinnetha, Illinois, in May, 1988, Lori Dan, thirty-year-old former mental patient, went on a shooting rampage, injuring six people and killing one. She had a long history of psychiatric treatment, and three psychiatrists stated that she had a severe psychotic disorder. She had a past history of many stabbings with an ice pick. One of the victims of this last shooting spree, Philip Andrew, recovered and asked, "Why was she out on the streets?"

In Norristown, Pennsylvania, August 1989, a former patient, D. Barr, drowned her three-year-old in a bathtub and was found by her husband sitting in the bathtub, holding the drowned child in her lap. He appeared on television the next evening and stated that his wife should get the death penalty. She had been treated while hospitalized for depression and probably had "post-partum depression." This was three years ago, and her illness probably surfaced after some situation precipitated her manifested illness.

No one knows what may trigger the onset of behavioral traits that may be manifested in the psyche of an individual.

In every community of the country, there are recorded deeds

of ex-mental patients. Often when catastrophies occur, it will be mentioned somewhere that the person had psychiatric treatment at sometime in their life.

Many people who have been treated for depression or other disorders related to some form of mental illness–or a "nervous breakdown" as it is often called–may never have a problem, as long as they adhere to the advice of their physician, take their medications or remove themselves from a situation that may be taxing or stressful. They should not be offended by the previous statement since these cases are usually relating to the recidivists discussed earlier.

Ms. Knight, still trying to close Westmont by the September deadline, told The Quest, "I'm seriously concerned about the care we're able to provide through a very difficult time. If things come to a crucial or critical point where patient safety is an issue, we will consider moving the patients to another state hospital."

Mr. Tweedil said, "The patients have little chance to go outside of their wards because the present staff is overwhelmed." He expressed concern for potential dehydration!

All of the patients who had ground privileges were outside! This was a complete lie told to the press by Tweedil, who really wasn't aware of what went on, as he had only visited the patients sporadically and thus could not make an accurate judgment. This statement however sounded good for the public and for the administrators. The summers were hot, without benefit of air conditioning, as discussed in an earlier statement, so why worry about the heat now? This was never a real concern for the state before!

The lawyers for the patients said that the state had been short-changing both the hospital and alternative community placements that were supposed to be created. "The state robs Peter to save Paul."

Unknown to the public, the state continues to lease or buy properties in the midst of communities throughout the city. The courts stand by the state's decision regardless of protests from the residents of those communities.

A three-story home was purchased by PATH (People Acting to Help), with plans to house nine mentally ill patients there. The residents protested, but their efforts failed and the zoning board approved the plans.

Even though the residents appealed the zoning decision to the Common Pleas Court, their objection was still rejected. PATH receives public financing——the tax payers' money——and yet these tax payers had no support from the judges, whose salaries are also paid by the tax payers.

PATH said that the community should have a better understanding of their dreams and goals; they were hopeful that it would result in a stable community, and they should be willing to work together with the community.

The neighbors wanted to know the level of supervision and security in the home, the types of patients to be housed there and the remedies available should these patients become problematic. The answer they received was that the patients would be manic depressives and schizophrenics, but would only be moved there if their symptoms were brought under control.

The conflict raged on! Common Pleas Court judge ruled in favor of PATH. The residents claimed they didn't get their day in court!

Meetings were held with the civic association and PATH, where there was an explanation of what mental illness is. Discussions of symptoms and characteristics did little to calm the fears of the residents. They were scared and didn't understand mental illness, and were concerned for the children in the neighborhood. They stated that because PATH had dealt with these people every day, they couldn't possibly understand the community's fears.

Some of the questions related to violent behaviors. PATH's answer was, "Anybody can become violent. People who are mentally ill may possibly be dangerous."

"What if they don't take their medications?"

"It depends on the individual," the PATH representative stated.

The community was not satisfied with that evening's discussion, and many questions remained unanswered. Everything stated in that meeting seemed evasive.

"Are we losing our rights?" asked the residents. "Even though a petition with sixteen hundred signatures was obtained against this maintenance house, the city and the state say we have to? Who is behind the push for PATH houses?"

A female patient with an assaultive background–and who had recently fractured two employees' noses and was placed in seclusion on many occasions–was now out there on the streets. She didn't like the house and living arrangements made by the state, and was placed in a hotel where she could live with her boyfriend. Guess who was paying the bill? The tax payers! This was another Bold Plan placement which can be attributed to Mary Knight. As she so often stated, "I know where every patient is placed, and they are being monitored very closely."

In San Francisco, California, a man was arrested after a bank robbery. He told police that voices told him to kill the president and he needed three thousand dollars to buy a motorcycle to go East and assassinate George Bush. He also stated that if he was not successful, he would kill children instead. These statements shocked the police; they said that when he started to talk, they realized that they had a very disturbed individual in their presence. The thirty-four-year old man, John Spencer Daughette, remained very calm and relaxed, and with good recall, when interviewed by the FBI. The idea of killing children was prompted by a television news broadcast which reported the shootings in Stockton. Patrick Edward Purdy had opened fire with a semiautomatic AK-47 in a schoolyard, killing five children and wounding twenty-nine students and one teacher. Daughette told the investigators that he had been treated in VA hospitals for mental problems, and that he had been interviewed by Secret Service authorities for alleged threats against ex-president Ronald Reagan. He admitted to the police that he had been stalking the president of the United States in an attempt to kill him. Voices told him that if he accomplished this task, he would be poisoned! But these voices did not tell him why!

This is just another scary tale of the truths being revealed here. Everyone will be at risk if this country does not treat the mentally ill in the proper facilities. This will not only protect the patients themselves, but society as a whole.

CHAPTER FIVE

On September 10, 1989, Sixty Minutes reported on a murder by a mental patient who is now interned in a state institution in Boston. Janice Spiro was diagnosed as mentally ill by the court psychiatrists, and was pronounced to be mentally unable to stand trial for the first degree murder of a friend, Jena Syndone. They were close friends and shared a house, and many thought that this was more than just a close relationship.

Jena was always involve in political and social causes. Her body was found floating face up in a bathtub, and it was evident that she had been strangled.

Janice was arrested and tried for her murder, with the defense attorney stating that she was mentally ill at the time. By reason of insanity, she was released to a mental institution for evaluation and treatment.

This murder happened in 1983 and, to this date, the parents of Jena want their justice and are still insisting on a trial. They believe that Janice was faking her illness.

Janice has a past history of drug and alcohol abuse and was arrested several times, once for car theft. She also has a history of suicide attempts.

The defense attorney still contended that the death of Jena was an accident. Janice's mother appeared with her daughter on a television show, hoping that this presentation would quell suspicions that her daughter was faking mental illness. It is only natural for a mother to want to protect her children, and now the public would know that Janice was ill and couldn't be responsible for past deeds.

They asked Janice about her relationship with Jena. She replied, "She was a——good——friend. I—loved and cared—for her." Her voice was shaky; she hesitated between words, and the jerky movements of her head and neck were quite visible to all.

"Not—strangled! Don't know—how she died. It's your—fault! It's not—real! None—of it!"

She had told a friend, Harry, that, "I strangled the bitch and put the body in the tub."

When asked by the TV host about this, she replied shakily, "I wasn't—there, I can't—hear what——you're saying!"

The defense lawyer was accused of presenting her in court in an unmedicated state to accentuate the mental disorder of his client.

Most people try to minimize their mental inconsistencies, but Janice appeared too mentally ill to go to court. She remains interned today.

Bruce Templeton, MD had been contracted by the state to evaluate patients for future placement in the community. An article talked about the Blue Ribbon Committee and the tasks that they would perform. In May, 1987, the Commonwealth of Pennsylvania appointed this task force to review the operations of Westmont, evaluate the treatment of the patients and also look into allegations of patient abuse.

Repeated criticisms in the press in the past decade prompted the formation of the committee regarding the "alleged abuse of patients." The committee sought assistance from Philadelphia psychiatrists to randomly review a sample of the patients. He was assigned two wards, and was to evaluate approximately seven patients on each ward.

Before he had a chance to begin his evaluations, he received a phone call asking him to go to a press conference on the grounds. The meeting was held by Mr. Whitman, who said that he was deeply concerned about the "widespread abuse of patients by the staff."

Preceding this conference, Mr. Whitman had been seen complimenting the hospital supervisory staff for working so devotedly under difficult conditions for many years.

Why would they bother to evaluate the treatment now when

their minds were made up to close the hospital? Would you treat a patient after he had died? This is the same concept. Dr. Templeton had not seen this type of abuse. He thought that the treatment seemed sufficient. The patients didn't appear as if they had been abused. The staff seemed interested in the welfare of their patients. The charts were informative and the records appeared to be satisfactory. But the hospital had already received its death sentence from the state officials.

"Au Revoir, Westmont", written by John A. Koltes, MD stated that reporters had produced in the public a sense of disgust about the hospital and the staff, and likened the hospital to the Holocaust: hopelessness and despair for the mentally ill, and, indeed, bad treatment–or worse, no treatment.

The abuse of the hospital by political and bureaucratic forces was noted by insufficient funds and pressure to keep undesirable employees. The administrations had seemed to change eight times within the last twelve years. Each new administration would come into their new posts, and the first thing each one did was change policies and procedures. The hospital never had a stable administration that was concerned about overall management, and it seemed as if the post was only a stepping stone to a higher position. They all had a different opinion about the role of hospital care for the mentally ill. The tension between the medical staff and the politicians contributed to the intense problems that plagued the hospital throughout its history.

A clinical nurse specialist listed the patients remaining at Westmont as "the worst of the psychotics and are the sickest, needing long-term care." As she walked through a ward, her first impression was that the aides were sitting around doing nothing. She attempted to start a card game with some of the patients to incite some activity. Shortly after the game began, tables were being overturned, and the patients were becoming assaultive. Something as simple as a card game had set them off. That's when she realized why the employees kept to themselves. "It's best to leave them alone, because you don't know when a patient will freak out," she said.

On an average day in a psychiatric unit you would see a nurse sitting at her desk, quietly glancing up now and then, making sure everything is in control. There would be a patient talking to no one on the telephone down the hall. Another patient passes by the screen window several times, standing momentarily and leering at her, then proceeding onward.

Another man is shadow boxing on the wall. Loud laughter rings from the dayroom, and investigation reveals one man giggling and laughing inappropriately, but happy nonetheless.

Some patients constantly wander in and out of the hallways on an endless expedition. Others walk with a fast gait, as if there was some place to go, asking, "What time is it?"

For some residents, the only highlight of the day is meal time or snacks; otherwise they would be seen curled up in a hair in the dayroom, as if everyone else was non-existent, hiding within themselves. Some patients constantly lie on the floor and are frequently requested to get up and use the furniture. There are also patients who will never wear shoes, no matter how much you encourage them.

Medication time arrives and patients line up at the window. This is the one time of the day that they feel that they have an identity. They are receiving personal attention when told to "open wide," assuring the nurse that they have taken their medication.

It appears that patients who act out once in a while gain the attention of the staff. This means that their names are never forgotten–everyone will remember the patient who went out of control. The old proverb remains true that "The squeaky wheel gets the oil." Patients become more agitated when demands are not met. Cigarettes appear to be the ultimate goal of most patients, either by bargaining with their peers, begging or stealing from others. Some patients had worked in the prep shop as a means of independence. This was terminated at the end of July, 1989. There are patients who become hostile, aggressive and assaultive towards peers while trying to obtain cigarettes. The activity groups usually used cigarettes as a means of reward for attendance in these groups. The patients knew that if they would attend the group session, cigarettes would be passed out at the end. When the Bingo games were played, they started with a minimal group. But when other patients saw the Bingo players coming back to the ward with cigarettes, more players would attend in an attempt to win this prize. This may keep a temporary peace on the wards.

These hard-core patients are cared for by the staff, who many times purchase cigarettes or sodas for the patients with their own money. Staff members have often brought in clothing from home for the patients to wear. Some of the patients have "pet" staff members that they look for daily. They also remember who treats them well.

As a society, we must get involved with our representatives and demand care for these people. How can these patients live in the community? What tragedies could be averted by not displacing these mentally ill people and by continuing to provide an institution for their care? These patients are people and should not be treated as less then human!

The end of June, 1989, was also significant, because Forensics was transferred as a unit to another state institution, bag and baggage. This was the major concern of neighbors who thought that the unit was threatening to them. The neighbors did not realize that the patients walking on the grounds were not the forensic patients, but were appropriate mental patients with ground privileges. The neighbors, their prejudices based on unfounded reasons, demanded to their representatives that these people be moved out. The forensic unit had been on the premises since 1974, but it was only after publicity from The Quest of the expansion of the unit that people really became aware of its existence. There was no way for these patients to escape, but still the neighbors feared the escape of patients. Not one of the neighbors was ever injured from the patients living on Westmont grounds.

On this bright, sunny day, many state troopers were present and buses were waiting. Many of the patients did not want to leave, but had no choice. Their legs were strapped in visible irons. This was done to prevent any escapes. Their hands were also cuffed. Two by two, they entered the buses while the staff stood by and watched.

There were feelings of sympathy and concern written all over the faces of the staff; apprehension and fear were exhibited by some. They had felt at home here, and the permanent staff was their pinnacle of security. Now they were leaving, being transferred to a new environment with a new staff, and wondering how they would be accepted. Some of these patients had been at Westmont for fifteen years.

The staff, unfortunately, was not also being transferred, but was absorbed within the general staff of the psychiatric units. The supervisor who had managed the forensic unit since its inception was so upset with the closing of her unit that she retired, disgusted with the state system.

Through the months of 1989, Booker and other dignitaries

often made rounds on the wards. Richter, although on the premises, did not appear as often as Booker. Wards would receive calls: "Visitors are coming; make sure that everything looks alright!"

Advocates for the mentally ill, important officials from the state capitol and mental health officials would walk through, showing a lack of manners. Rarely did they acknowledge the staff or say "Good Morning." Rarely did they introduce themselves, and there were times when the staff had to ask who they were. If you asked a question or made a remark, their answer was always very blunt.

So often did these calls come and no one would arrive that the staff became indifferent to these messages and could care less if people came. To the staff, these calls only meant that the administrators didn't think that they were doing their job and wanted them to appear busy. This was good for their image. Little did the administrators know that they could rely on their staff for information about the patients in their care.

The administration had never supported its staff, even in the difficult times of stress, anxiety and overwork when some staff members weren't sure if they would have a job after the closure.

Many doctors were furloughed, and the few on staff were condensing medical and psychiatric services. There were a few physician who refused to perform both services to protect their licenses. The remaining physicians were also getting disgusted of the obviously disorganized administrative decisions handed down. Some doctors refused to be puppets of the state and departed. Although clinical meetings would stress that "the patients come first, the patient's care is the first priority," these were only words that one would expect to be uttered, devious prefabrications, a smoke screen to hide the real truth: "They didn't care and they wanted to close the hospital!"

What now remained at Westmont were the hard-core mentally ill. There have been times when medical problems arose that necessitated the transfer of a patient to the nearest general hospital. They have had some problematic patients who were at times uncooperative, and these professionals were also afraid of our patients. A staff member always accompanied the patient as a reassurance to both the patient (as a friendly face) and the general hospital staff. Our patients' behavior many times were inappropriate, with outbursts and yelling accompanied by Tardive Dyskenesia, or jerky movements, which could intimidate the professionals in the general hospital.

The directors of the general hospital staff met with our administration to discuss our admissions to their facility. They felt uncomfortable and at times insecure and fearful of our clients, and requested that they not be sent there except in a life-threatening situation. A list of more than seventy patients was issued to the wards of patients who definitely could not be sent to this outside facility.

As stated before, these people are ill, and it is not their fault; yet the public is afraid of what it does not understand. The staff of Westmont know their patients and how to treat them like no one else.

This next case will leave no doubt as to what the term "hardcore" means. Patients like this one can never return to community living and need a facility such as Westmont.

At the age of twenty-six, Paul was admitted to Westmont from another hospital after blinding himself with a sharp instrument and removing his right eye with his fingers. The previous year, before he destroyed his right eye, he poured lye into his left eye. When physicians told him at that time that they could save his eye, he tore it out completely with his fingers. He stated later that he regretted it.

He had a long history of self-mutilation. He had bitten off part of his tongue, which caused a speech impediment. He slit his throat and both wrists. He pulled on his testicles stating, "They have to come off!"

Paul had three brothers and two sisters, all of whom became educated, and a few were on the honor roll at school. The oldest brother excelled in school and sports and seemed to do everything right, thus gaining the most attention and affection from the mother. It was quite evident to Paul that his brother was favored, and the mother admitted this in open conversations.

Hatred and jealousy swelled, overpowering Paul's emotions at times, as he tried to tolerate when his brother received the adoration and praise from the family. Paul always felt that he was neglected by his mother, and thus turned his affections more toward his father, to whom he became very close and dependent on.

Paul had to be forced to go to high school and he seemed to travel with the "bad crowd," the truants and tough guys. He always associated with older boys and incorrigibles.

He was more interested in jobs and making money than

getting an education. His father was a college graduate, and his mother had finished high school before getting married. She was treated for post-partum psychosis after delivering her third child and spent three weeks in the hospital.

Paul tried LSD at the age of sixteen and had a "bad trip," leaving him hospitalized for six days. He also had a history of sniffing glue and abusing cocaine. At the age of sixteen, he ran away from home with a best friend who was a big time drug dealer. They ended up in California and, at the age of seventeen, he impregnated a girl and married her. The marriage only lasted one and one-half years, when his wife met another man and divorced Paul, taking her son with her.

Odd jobs compensated his living needs, with one position lasting three years until he became argumentative with the son of his employer, and he was let go.

Paul had been delusional in the past, believing that, "They were out to get his family." We think that he meant the Mafia, and that he felt self-mutilation would be his sacrifice to save his family. At least that was the reason he had given to the therapists.

One of the first incidents that lead to Paul's psychiatric hospitalization included purchasing a gun and threatening to shoot his father and brother. With verbal intervention, he was talked out of this idea; he then ran quickly up the stairs to his room and emptied the gun into the door.

Paul stated that he was mentally ill and that he belonged in an institution, and if there was any attempt to place him into the community, he would commit suicide. He also believed that forces of good and evil existed within him, and when they became off balance, he would become mentally ill.

He was aware of his surroundings and remembered the names of the staff and doctors. He got around quite well with his cane and, because he maneuvered about the ward with such familiarity, it appeared at times that he could see where he was going. His intellect was within normal limits, and his ability to manipulate the staff was evident. He appeared to make adjustments, but these were only superficial. His behavior changes could be unpredictable. His regression back to self-mutilation and his psychotic states continue to be problematic. His relaxed appearance and the fragility of his delusions focused warnings to the staff of impending behaviors. For instance:

1) Diet– Change to just eating vegetables
2) Drink excessive amount of water
3) Sporadic sleep habit
4) Social withdrawal
5) Overly suspicious

Paul was placed on twenty-four hour supervision when these traits surfaced in his behavioral pattern.

The staff knew the patients and would observe these unusual changes, and often–although not always–could prevent episodes or incidents from occurring.

Many of the psychiatric aides were "long termers" and had worked within the system for many years. They had experience in dealing with these patients and had also built a good rapport with most of them. They knew what could be considered "normal" for their patients. Their observations of any deviation from their "norm" would quickly be reported to their supervisor.

The nurse, the doctor and the other disciplines could rely on data supplied by the aides because they remained with the patients continuously during their shift, day after day.

Care, control and custody were their assignments. Many of these patients lacked survival skills and could not exist on their own without direction and supervision. The aides provided this. Their duties were three fold. They showered and shaved, dressed and undressed, gave nourishment and fluids, monitored and observed, accompanied to clinics, played games, did charting, spot-cleaned incontinency occurred and were the overall babysitters of the wards. They never received the recognition they deserved, especially from the media, whose only descriptive word for them was "abusers." These aides were the only family some of the patients had!

As in any institutional setting (hospital, nursing home, boarding home, half-way house, etc.), forms of abuse can occur. But abuse also occur in families with children, wives and older parents.

Although not reported in the newspapers, there is an investigative committee on staff to interrogate and record statements given to hem by patients or witnesses. If a charge of abuse was founded, the abuser would be reprimanded and released.

The hospital monitored itself and stressed the consequences if a confirmed case of abuse was established. The abuse included verbal as sell as physical, as well as unnecessary punishment or denial. The staff would think twice before any though of abuse entered their minds. Yes! This was a deterrent for the staff, and they would not be allowed to take out their frustrations on the patients.

The human race consists of different personalities and temperaments, tolerance and frustration levels. In any case, abuse would sporadically be reported and investigated, with disciplinary action carried out when warranted.

In case after case discussed her, you have been given examples of the terms "hard-core" or terminally ill mental patient, and these are the people that the state is trying to place in your community. These are the people who have been treated with every known therapies. These are the people who have not responded positively to any known medication or therapy.

Remember the consumer advocates, who are largely responsible for the deinstitutionalization movements in this country, have had some positive response to their treatments and are now able to function in society because of it. Many of these advocates were hospitalized, and if it weren't for their treatment in these facilities, they might never have had the opportunity to function in society again.

The television talk show hosts who discuss the topic of mental illness and have as their guests some of these consumer advocates have yet to balance their shows with the other side: the families of these hard-core recidivists who can never go home again. They have yet to relate their experiences and frustrations in direct discussion with these advocates. As the public views these shows on television, they become horrified and angry at the system without understanding the true consequences a family must endure when they have a relative who is severely afflicted with mental illness.

The advocates denounce their treatment and medication routine while interned, and yet they have no understanding of the therapy involved. No doubt that incidents of overdose by some psychiatrists were recorded, and there is no doubt that all doctors are competent. Society always produces the good with the bad in all professions, but one should not judge all by a few. It is doubtful that all of the advocates had insight into their own illnesses. Naturally when they feel that they are functioning well, they feel that they are cured! As stated previously, schizophrenia is only controlled, not cured. It could be compared to the illness of a diabetic: without insulin or other medications, they will relapse the same as the mentally ill.

After viewing several television shows relating to mental illness, Morton Downey said, "Down with psychiatry. Down with the psychiatrists." He stated that if psychiatry was a medicine or a drug, it would be banned by the FDA. The audience consisted mostly of people with histories of mental illness in one form or another. Little did he know that mental illness is not a blanket term for all behaviors. There are many variations and types of behaviors, fitting into different classifications of the disease. He did not know the histories or backgrounds of these people, and took their word that they were all mistreated or overdosed on medication. The picture portrayed was that of people placed into institutions without cause. Did he know what precipitated these actions? Do you think that some of these people would actually relate the details which lead to confinement? Did he ask if they had attempted suicide or inflicted injuries on others?

As he concluded his show, he ran off the stage shouting, "To hell with psychiatry and the psychiatrists. If you are over eighteen, don't let them put you away!"

He had Jim Smith, who was discussed earlier in this book and who was responsible for the firing of Mr. Randall, as one of his guest. He didn't display any frustrations while on the program, because the show was one-sided and in his favor. The professional guests that appeared on that program were not given a chance to speak because of the hostilities displayed by the advocates. The show was a real disgrace, as it related to a subject that Mr. Downey knew nothing about.

We would suggest that he take a tour in an institution where the hard-core mental patients exist. We suggest that before he places a program on the television, that he gain the proper information first. The public views these programs and can be swayed by this sort of misinformation.

We are glad that the advocates can resume their place in society, but what they don't realize is that a certain percent of patients are not as fortunate as they are!

Sally Jesse Raphael also had a program on television relating to mental illness and, as Morton Downey, didn't know about the subject, sympathized with her guests and their treatments, and only infuriated the professionals who care for these individuals.

Dennis Woltering of Channel Ten News was a reporter who did an investigative report titled, "Committed to the Streets," and told the truth about the problems developing in the communities due to the deinstitutionalization process. His show was informative and real! He not only interviewed some ex-patients on the streets, but also showed the hardships and frustrations endured by the families.

It is only lately that the media is making the public aware of the existence of mental illness. As stated before, the public doesn't know, and they don't care!

A deranged man in Louisville, Kentucky, went on a shooting rampage in his former place of employment. He had been placed on permanent disability due to a mental disorder and problems which arose during his term of employment.

During the shooting spree, he killed seven people and injured thirteen others before taking his own life. He had reportedly continued to threaten the company, and blamed them for his lack of work.

Joseph Wesbecker, forty-seven years old, took an AK 47 semiautomatic rifle from his duffel bag an opened fire. He was looking for the "bosses or supervisors"; because he couldn't find any, he opened fire and shot at everything that was close to him.

Wesbecker was argumentative and confrontational for many years. He was considered paranoid and felt that everyone was out to get him. He lacked insight into his illness and blamed everyone else for his troubles. It is not known whether he was taking his medications. He was not only troubled, but could not control his emotions or behavior.

This was not the fault of the gun, but the man behind the trigger. He had always told fellow workers that he'd be back, which only enforces the premeditated, bizarre, threatening ideas he had entertained in his distorted thought processes.

In August, 1989, an extensive study was done entitled, "Looking for Schizophrenia in the Brain." A clinical research center at the University of Pennsylvania allowed the opportunity to re-search identical twins, one with normal behaviors and the other diagnosed with schizophrenia.

They were both raised with three other brothers, and there was no history of schizophrenia in their family. At the age of nineteen, one of the twins developed schizophrenia and stated, "There was an explosion in my head. I got confused and imagined I was bleeding in my head. I saw things and heard voices that talked to me."

Schizophrenia can strike one in one hundred people, and it

usually occurs in the late teens or early twenties. It usually hits people who are about to embark on a new career, and turns them into non-productive, dependent individuals.

Environment did not seem to be a contributing factor in this case, as all of the children experienced their childhood in the same household and no one else was effected. Twenty or thirty years ago, disturbing experiences were believed to precipitate schizophrenic traits.

Schizophrenia is one of the most common and disabling forms of mental illness. Over one-third recover spontaneously, while two-thirds continue to live in the bizarre world of delusions and hallucinations.

Science has developed remarkable imaging devices and laboratory techniques to allow researchers to actually see the human brain as it processes information and emotions. Comparisons can be made between the brains of sick and healthy people. The University of Pennsylvania and St. Elizabeth Hospital in the District of Columbia are the only institutions in the country doing such research on twins.

The National Institute of Mental Health (NIMH) provided a three-year grant to the University of Pennsylvania. In only five years, the grant was increased from $18.7 million in 1985 to $44.6 million in 1989.

In November, 1988, University of London researchers reported that in a study in England and Iceland, they had identified a gene that had lead to schizophrenia in seven families. The current therapy for schizophrenia is at best hit or miss and may involve years of ineffective treatment.

No conclusive evidence was drawn from the research by comparing these two twins, and the results from this work will probably end up as only a paragraph or two on a research paper; but it did provide more support to the growing theory that schizophrenia is an organic brain disease.

The brains of these twins were examined with PET, Position Emission Tomography; CAT, Computerized Axial Tomography; and MRI, Magnetic Resonance Imaging. These tests were conceded to be disappointing in that they did not reveal differences; however PET did find a difference in the basal ganglia (nerve tissues at the base of the brain) involved in subconscious regulation of movement, emotions, intellectual processes and other functions. The twin with schizophrenia denoted that the cells of the ganglia were working harder than the cells in the cerebral cortex, the part of the brain responsible for higher functions such as thought, memory and language.

This meant that the cortex was working less than it should be. In schizophrenia the cortical activity is significantly lower than average. Experimentation still goes on!

The cause of schizophrenia remain a guessing game: What exact mixture of genetic influence, heredity, environment or chemical imbalances can create this condition in an individual? Researchers and scientists continue to explore all avenues referring to the human mind or make-up. Early signs of chemical brain changes might be clues to impending schizophrenia and manic depression. Researchers developed anti-psychotic drugs to treat these conditions which helped about sixty percent of schizophrenics; many of these chemicals transmitted nerve impulses to the brain.

Anti-depressants used to treat mania, such as lithium carbonate, alter the tolerance of other neurotransmitters and bring relief to a vast majority of sufferers. Psychiatrists are also trying to find proof of heredity as being a contributing factor to mental illness. It is known that in some families, there is a definite set of symptoms repeated form one generation to the next.

Researchers are tracking down the genes that may predispose illness, but because all mental illnesses involve different complex behaviors, experts are not certain that a genetic predisposition will be as simple as a single abnormal gene.

The question of "Nature vs. Nurture" was addressed by Dr. Jack Grebb of New York University Medical Center: "Schizophrenia may result from prenatal events." An example would be infection by a virus which could effect the fetus genetically, making it susceptible to the illness.

Let us not forget to mention the alcohol and drug abusers, who pass on to the fetus the threat of further addiction or behavioral problems relating to these additions.

We've named some very tragic and serious incidents which have happened to placed patients, and there are more waiting to happen. In August, 1989, two events would happen which would put a halt to future placements of patients from Westmont. These two tragedies would force state officials taking another look at the reality of their plan. First of all, these officials did not understand the complexities of schizophrenia; secondly, they did not have the necessary hands-on experience. They were dealing in "numbers of individuals," not the difference types of personalities and behaviors exhibited by schizophrenics: Each one certainly is an individual, and each one is different. Each one behaves differently in a situation, and each one is triggered by different occurrences.

John Keller, discussed earlier in this book, who was discharged through the courts and painted his mother's house with gloss enamel paint, drowned in the Schulykill River. His decomposed body was discovered below the South Street Bridge after he had disappeared from a group home. His mother pleaded many times to have her son admitted for treatment. He had come home on a daily basis from his group home, and had once turned on the gas and left the house. He was seen wandering in traffic in the rain, appearing unaware of where he was. His condition was deteriorating, and he was only taking his medication sporadically.

John's mother said, "The state promised to put people where they could get the help they needed. It just wasn't the way it was supposed to be!"

Eight days later, Joe was pulled from the same river, dead from drowning. The body looked as if it had been beat up and thrown in the river.

Joe suffered from brain damage, attributed to a fall from a tree at the age of thirteen. He had been in a coma for a long period of time after the fall, losing the ability to walk of speak. This traumatic injury would change his whole productive life. He was not considered schizophrenic but, due to organic brain trauma, portrayed bizarre, erratic, assaultive, uncontrollable behavior.

He was cared for by his parents until his father died and his mother entered a nursing home due to medical problems. He was placed in Westmont because his siblings could not handle his behavior problems and could not control him in their homes.

Joe was placed into the community on a trial basis, but residents of that community opposed the placement, complained to their committeeman and representatives, and the state was forced to remove him. He was then sent to Harbor House and was placed on a one-to-one observation and supervision. People noticed that he was out on the streets more than he was in the house.

Joe never followed the rules of any placement home where he was placed, and his behavior was never controlled. This was enough reason for rejection by other programs, for he had many problems and no one knew how to deal with them.

Joe's sister told Richter, "He doesn't belong in the community. He needs a secure environment. Everyone knows it! A hospital——someplace that he can't get out of!" Once when he had eloped, he returned home with the police and exhibited a black eye, appeared beat up, and had no shoes on. Before the drowning incident, he had eloped again and returned two days later displaying a long, deep laceration above his eyebrow.

Both cases raised questions about the intensive care of these chronically mentally ill patients. Were they better off in the community, or should they remain hospitalized?

The Quest reported on its front page that two ex-patients drowned in the river. Could this headline conceive another avenue of suicide thought of by yet another patient who might read this paper? It probably did, for that evening, Pat decided to jump from a bridge into the same river. She was lucky to be seen when this occurred, and was saved by the police. She was a recent placement and had a background of assaultive behavior. She had been expelled from her placement house for assaulting another patient there, and was later arrested for attacking a police officer with a lead pipe. When standing in front of the judge, she stated that she was a patient from Westmont, said that she was sorry and would not do this again. "Please let me go back to my house! I didn't know what I was doing!" The judge listened sympathetically to her begging and allowed her request.

Perhaps in her twisted way of thinking, and not having a feeling of security, the idea of jumping into the river may have appealed to her. After all, two others had done this. Why not her?

We have had a series of jumping in front of trains, and now the trend seemed to be jumping off of bridges.

John Keller and Joe belonged to the same CTT team that was supposed to ensure a safe alternative to institutionalizing, by providing and monitoring their treatment seven days a week around the clock.

Richter, Knight and hospital administrators could not be reached for comment the day the press released news to the public. Mary Knight told the press the next day, "I think we have to look at this to see what mistakes we made and what we could have done differently. We need to examine how we assure that people are going to be safe."

Did it really have to take all of this time and all of these incidents to produce such a statement? Again the administration was trying to cover the bungling of their placement program. "We tried to provide adequate supervision," Knight said.

There would now be many questions to answer concerning the "Bold Plan of Community Placement." Cornered by their own incompetency, Knight and Richter would have to make statements to the public: What would they say? What could they say?

Knight announced her decision to order an outside investigation into these two deaths. The city would conduct their own investigation. She finally acknowledged that, "Mistakes may have been made." She spoke with emotion and said, "It was a tragedy." She still insisted that her staff had worked diligently with these patients.

Yes! This was a real tragedy! Were not the other hidden incidents real tragedies also? What about Ronald and Marion, who were killed when they jumped in front of trains? Where were all of the other tragic events which were not publicized and did not require emotions to be exhibited? It is only when cornered that they have to display concern.

Three weeks before these two drownings, the governor agreed to meet with some of the family members. It was stipulated that only three people would be admitted to that meeting. This meeting came about because of persistent phone calls by the families to the governor's hot line on a daily basis, and it became clear that these calls would continue until the promise of this meeting was fulfilled. The governor had made a public commitment to this meeting, and the families were going to hold him to it!

The meeting was arranged for August 30, 1989. Mr. Randall would not be one of the participants, because his case was in litigation. This was the firing that occurred after the talk radio show.

August 30, 1989, the date set for the families' meeting with the governor just so happened to fall on the heels of these last two drowning deaths and another attempt by another mental patient who was placed by Westmont's administrative staff. These events, although tragic, were advantageous for the families in stressing the urgency of their plight.

This was also a traumatic blow for the CTT programs, and the newspaper exposure of these two events would become a turning point in the reality of the present placement program. The families' conference with the governor included the mother of John Keller and the brother of the victim.

The families came prepared with a list of requests, and

handed them to the governor. This meeting, which was scheduled to last only one-half hour, lasted one and and one-half hours. The families had information of many incidents that had occurred and also listed the names of these mentally ill patients. The governor appeared astonished, and the consensus was at that time that he had not been informed by his officials of all of the incidents and listened intently to their sagas.

He seemed angry when he learned of the removal of the statue of St. Dymphna, the patron saint of the mentally ill. It appeared that Knight and Richter had not kept him abreast of all the issues. It was either ignorance or play acting, but the families were convinced that he didn't know.

Everyone had been blaming the governor and Whitman for the disorganization and happenings, but the men were only making decisions upon the information received from their appointed staff.

The same afternoon of this memorable meeting, the governor made a very important announcement on the evening news: That the closing of Westmont would be suspended indefinitely, until further investigations about the patients who were already placed were made. They would review the closing program and follow-up on patients already released. He did not want to place communities and patients in jeopardy.

Elated staff members permeated the atmosphere at Westmont. This was the first time in ages that the staff's morale was boosted. As soon as some of the patients realized what the announcement meant, it was hoped that their anxieties would also subside.

This small battle between families, staff and lawyers appeared won. Tensions would be eased, at least temporarily.

These two tragic events made martyrs of Joe and John and would seemingly protect their peers from the same fate.

A new beginning! A new life! This was the elated feeling of everyone on staff. Westmont would now take one breathe at a time, move one arm, then one leg, until we could repair all of the damages done!

The hospital had been brutalized and stigmatized by both previous administrations and the media, and now it was up to all the staff to prove them wrong. There was much work to do.

The disciplines–housekeeping, dietary, recreation, prep shop, activities–had to be returned. They had been slowly diminished and halted, and replacing them could not be done overnight.

One thing we could do was to weed out unproductive personnel who didn't perform and who weren't interested in their positions. We wanted to prove to everyone, even the media, that Westmont could work with a little effort and funding from the state. We could care for and treat the remaining chronically ill patients. We could be their protectors.

The pillar of hope was the trust and loyalties of the patients' families which could carry the hospital into a new realm of satisfaction. The families had won this first battle, and what a battle it was, with the shedding of many tears, twisted senses of anxieties and frustration, and finally a feeling of relief and serenity.

With Lois Booker as the new superintendent, questions were asked: "What's she like? Does she really care now? Does she really want the position or will she be like the rest of the administrators, overcome with her own feelings of power from this new position?"

She had talked about retiring in October, but now she was heard to say, "Wait until I tell my husband that I'm the top administrator of this hospital!"

As the word was passed from ward to ward, the response was the same: "Oh No! Oh No!"

Booker now felt that she was in the good graces of the governor's administration, and also hinted exuberantly that she could probably get any position she wanted in the state.

This was ironic, as she was just as responsible for placing patients into the community as Richter and Knight. The incidents that had happened were partly her fault for recommending their release. Now she was placed into the position of superintendent, which totally disgusted the staff and the families. What a poor choice for the patients!

Did she really earn this position by placing unacceptable patients into the community, many of which had bad experiences? Was there no one from within the realm of the hospital to take this position? It had never been offered, but was simply another political appointment! The staff decided to be tolerant and give her a chance, as it was the only choice they had.

Ethel Richter, it was learned, was no longer on the community placement program and was transferred to support the CTT program. Everyone waited to see how much power Mary Knight had. Would her services no longer be needed? What would be her next move? Would it be to close another, smaller hospital? Everyone wished that she would return to Ohio, from where she had come.

Ethel Richter was given a high position on the city's payroll in their Office of Mental Health. It seems that in politics, if you blunder they get rid of you by rewarding with another position somewhere else!

Mary Knight, it was learned, although still in the state system, would no longer be associated with the "Bold Plan of Community Placement." Now there were two down, and one to go. Lois Booker should have been removed as the superintendent of Westmont. The families would soon focus their requests in this direction.

Mr. Formbe, who presided over the family support group, aroused the group support of the reinstatement of Mr. Randall, the social worker who had been fired from his job by the bureaucrats for voicing his opinion about the decision to close the hospital. This would be the group's next priority.

The governor called for a review of the closure program, including those patients already released into the community. He also wanted a re-evaluation of the process that determines the need for a patient's further hospitalization or his or her ability to function in a community setting. He asked Mr. Whitman to form an assessment team to evaluate each patient who had already been discharged and ordered an investigation into the incidents which had already occurred. The governor wanted some answers!

Lois booker, who was now the hospital administrator, would help to orchestrate these assessments, and orders were given to the CTT members to complete these evaluations and hand in their papers by the Tuesday after Labor Day. This would only be five days after the announcement that the hospital would indefinitely remain open until results were in. Although these results would not be printed in the newspaper until two weeks later, it appeared that the teams worked hard to comply with the governor's request.

It wouldn't take a genius to figure out that these assessments would be hastily done to comply with Lois Booker's mandate. The information would be filled out, of course, but completed forms would not record accurate information. This was nothing more than a mock assessment that kept patients at risk, due to the shoddy and sometimes falsified information on these forms.

It was another job hastily done by the officials whose past performance was nicely covered up by the media.

The governor would rely on their findings to make his final decision as to the closure of Westmont. His subordinates would hand him these quickie, inaccurate assessments in order to reinforce his original decision to close. After all, they didn't wish to appear inefficient, even though their "Bold Plan of Placements" was a failure thus far.

I wonder what information was written on the forms of a few of the cases:

1) M.G.–After discharge, jumped from a second story window and died.
2) M.L.–Known suicidal tendency–tried to jump from a bridge, but was rescued by a passerby.
3) J.K.–Returned to the hospital and raped a female patient. Ended up in the jails.
4) J.C.–Was raped by a discharged patient who had returned to the grounds.
5) T.G.–Discharged by the courts; committed suicide in a river.
6) B.K.–Was placed, but continues to cost the state money by tearing up supermarkets, drugstores and restaurants, and who needs five staff members around the clock daily to control him.
7) D.T.–Discharged and then committed suicide by jumping in front of a subway train.
8) M.r.–Eloped and killed herself by jumping in front of a subway train.
9) M.L.–Died in a second floor apartment after being placed there with a severe heart condition.
10) J.R.–Discharged by the courts; ended up beaten severely in a community hospital.
11) D.D.–Was discharged and found unconscious on the side walk.
12) G.A.–Was placed in a hotel to live with her boyfriend because she didn't like the house that was picked for her to live in.
13) S.S.–Attacked staff members and was recommitted to another state facility.
14) A.T.–Placed in house, but is afraid to stay there; called the hospital nightly for reassurance from the staff.
15) W.G.–Placed in boarding house, complains that he is afraid of being beaten if he doesn't sign his check over to his keepers.
16) E.J.–Pushed a woman in front of an oncoming train; after the trial, he was committed to jail instead of receiving psychiatric care in an institution.
17) E.S.–Seen disheveled and dirty, with a significant weight loss noted.
18) B.F.–Discharged to apartment and was seen on the television

doing well on her own, then was found overdosed on the streets.

19) A.C.–Was seen by staff members strung out on drugs and l iving on the streets.

20) J.G.–Found drowned in the river.

21) P.S.–Attempted to drown herself in the river but was saved.

22) J.T.–Found drowned in a creek.

23) D.B.–Attacked a police officer and was killed; the officer also died from his stab wounds.

24) G.D.–Seen by staff members digging into garbage cans and eating trash.

25) I.H.–Found wandering nude in a public park; was picked up by the police.

These are only a few episodes involving the discharged patient. Many more are unknown or unpublicized. There were also numerous ex-patients who were trying to be readmitted but were turned away.

The S.P.C.A. will travel across the city to pick up a sick or dying animal, but human beings are allowed to kill themselves or lie all over the streets, some of them starving and exposed to all of the elements. These are human beings!

The reprieve of closure by the governor lightened our spirits, and, perhaps, there was a chance at last for Westmont to remain open to care for these chronic mental patients.

Although there was a suspension of closing, the admission unit would remain closed. Patients returning for admission were rejected, of course. They reminded me of homing pigeons coming home to roost.

Just after the announcement was made, several ex-patients returned to grounds. One even walked all the way from Lerner's State Hospital, which was more than twenty miles away. After several hours, Lois Booker arranged for his transportation back by a security car, with one aide to accompany him.

Only the night before, Jack had been picked up on the grounds, his head bleeding from a beating he had received before coming back to Westmont. He appeared anxious for protection, and his fearful facial expression turned to one of thankful sanction. Jack could not talk due to some malady, and thus could not relate what had happened to him. But he made motions with his hands and grunted, as if to try to tell us that someone had hit him on the head.

The wound was cleansed, and the bleeding stopped.

Jack was in his late fifties and had a frail frame. He was neatly dressed with clean trousers and shirt, but his light tan jacket was spattered with blood from the head trauma. The watch on his left wrist reported the right time.

The psychiatrist tried to explain to him that we were closed for admission, and that he could not stay. Jack shook his head, and you could see the disappointment in his face; it was evident that he wanted to stay.

"Where do you live? How did you get here? Did you walk? Why did you come here?" All of the questions went unanswered and received only outstretched arms, pointed fingers or nods of his head.

The crisis center was called, but they refused to come out stating, "We have two 302's, and we're too busy right now. Take him to Harbor or Kindley Hospital. Aren't they closer?"

The caring nurse and guard did not want to place him on a bus. For God's sake! What could happen to him? He can't talk or explain anything! The decision was made. He would be driven to Harbor Hospital and left at the emergency room where he would at least be safe and receive care. They wouldn't turn him out, would they? Jack was given a note saying: "My name is Jack Stanley."

This was the second time in three months that Jack had returned to Westmont to be readmitted. "He doesn't belong out there. This is the place for him to be," said the guard . "He's always getting beat up out there," he added. "It's a real shame!"

What are we doing to these helpless, confused individuals who really need care? Why are they turned out into the streets time and time again? Then the media bombards the public with questions like: "Why is the homeless situation getting worse?"

Need we ask that question? We are all aware of the reasons yet remain silent and just complain about it.

Mentally ill people commit suicide or wander off because the treatment services are not out there in the communities. Hospital care should be accessible to all people who are in crisis and need treatment, regardless of their ability to pay.

Due to the overcrowding of the metropolitan hospitals, they are finding it necessary to shut their doors on the mentally ill. A fifty-eight-year-old woman in crisis was placed in a boarding home and had probably not been taking her medications. Suicidal ideas began to arise, accompanied by hallucinations of voices telling her to hurt herself.

She verbally threatened suicide, and then disappeared from her placement, causing great concern.

The police were alerted and found a confused, disoriented woman, who was responding to internal stimuli, walking along the railroad tracks of one of the busiest intersections. With much persuasion, they rescued her and accompanied her to one of the well-known urban hospitals.

They were turned away because "she wasn't one of theirs." She had belonged to another catchment area, one of thirteen which served the city. A catchment area is an area in which the patient lives in a certain section of the city, where all residents in that community have a designated area and were obligated to use it.

The hospital had gone on "restriction" status at 1:00P.M., which meant that it was too crowded to handle any more involuntary psychiatric patients. The police were told to take her to another hospital, but it just so happened that the other hospital also had gone on restricted status. The hospital spokesman blamed the overcrowding on the psychiatric emergency rooms and shortage of psychiatric beds in community hospitals.

He also blamed the closing of admissions at Westmont, the city's only long term psychiatric hospital. The number of drug and alcohol related crises which were now being handled in the emergency rooms were a contributory factor to the overcrowding in the community hospitals.

This proved the shortcomings of the city's emergency services for the mentally ill. The burgeoning demand on those limited services was all the more reason to keep Westmont open!

On one evening alone, one psychiatric emergency room was handling seven 302's (involuntary commitments), and had a full house.

These are the reasons for "restricting," which in time may conspire to close all of the emergency psychiatric services in the city. "Every one is full!" "Every one is frustrated!" "Every one is diverting from one part of the city to another."

In New York in 1988, overcrowding had reached record levels, and the mental system is moving towards disaster. No longer can assurances be given as to the safety of the patients and the staff in the emergency rooms.

At Bellevue Hospital, four staff members were injured in separate incidents while trying to subdue disturbed patients.

An alcoholic treatment center at one hospital was turned into a makeshift psychiatric center.

At King's County Hospital, four patients were seen handcuffed to the armrests of wheelchairs as they waited for beds. Three or four others lounged on the benches. Cots were set up at night so they could sleep while waiting for admission. Patients had to sleep in shifts due to the shortage of beds.

Another newspaper in a different city reported that ever since the state hospitals were emptied out in the seventies, society has been unable to come up with enough funds or enough compassion to construct a satisfactory alternative.

Mayor Koch of New York was trying to force his city, and the nation, to pay attention to the "shameful neglect of our homeless, mentally ill." Both morally and legally, we have an obligation to help those who cannot or will not help themselves.

CHAPTER SIX

A state representative whose constituents lived in the hospital area would speak out of both sides of his mouth. Even though he was on the land use committee, he still wanted to seem concerned about the situation at Westmont. He had to address the chaotic situation of released patients, and sympathized with the tragic events that had occurred.

He suggested that everything be done in the communities to meet the services and needs of these individuals; on the other hand, he still favored the closing of Westmont. He was, after all, working for his constituents who voted him into office. He could not chance losing their votes, and yet he could not condone the deaths of discharged patients.

Everyone knew that his was not a genuine concern for the patients, and the underlying reason for his expressed sympathies were political. His real concern was like that of many politicians, that of retaining the support of the voters who always returned him to his post.

The families had tried on at least five different occasions to meet with him, but he was never available to them and never acknowledged their calls. It seemed as if he were avoiding the meeting and did not want to get involved in the situation. This was a great disappointment to the families, coming as it did from one of their representatives in the state.

This representative, "Mr. K.," stated publicly that, "Concerned citizens were supplying [him] with a series of allegations and accusations, rumors and concerns about patient treatment at Westmont, as well as the mismanagement of the hospital staff itself." It was doubtful that he had received any information of this sort, but these remarks would please his voters. It was simply another twist in his plot to help close Westmont.

The auditorium roof, which was leaking, was at last going to be repaired after much squabbling about whose responsibility it was. They had considered this structure a danger because of the roof, and the work was contracted out by the state. The developers were worried about the heating problem which would occur when the hospital closed. The entire place was heated by a central power plant which would naturally be shut down. The land use committee was still proposing a golf course with housing clusters near it. They were also considering housing for the elderly; medical centers or medical offices; a corporate park with three or four buildings with three or four floors, surrounded by twenty acres of greenery.

While the committees bickered over the division of the land and the purposes for which it would be used, another patient was discovered drowned in a creek. Now there had been three drownings and one attempted drowning. All of these incidents had occurred in one month. The governor's decision to keep Westmont open indefinitely worried the land developers, as it would put a crimp in their plans.

Mr. Whitman insinuated in the press that, "Someone was running around...this was something other than a coincidence...there may be something else at play..." Was he suggesting that the hospital staff was pushing these discharged patients into the river in order to keep the hospital open? What a disgraceful accusatory statement to make. This was the kind of thinking and performance eminating from our representative in the state.

"I think it warrants further investigation by the D.A." The city's homicide investigator expressed surprise at these statements and said that "There was absolutely nothing to indicate foul play in any of these deaths." They all drowned and none had any injury. Homicide by drowning is rare."

Shortly after the governor's announcement, the acting superintendent would be relieved of his duties, and guess who was placed in that position? It was Lois Booker! A decision which would determine whether the hospital would stay open or still be designated for closure would be forthcoming by the end of September.

The bets were on! Everyone was asking the same questions, and many rumors floated around.

What a poor choice for an administrator! Families felt that this woman was a danger to their families; they would soon attempt to have her removed from this position. Westmont had always been the abused child of the state, with numerous administrations that didn't care and who didn't want to be there in the first place.

The families felt that in the past, the position only upgraded these officials in the field of political appointments; and when they reached this pinnacle, they lost concern for the patients, and also lost prospective of their reason for being there in the first place. Their position at Westmont only boosted their list of qualifications on their resumes and their salaries. Many were not qualified and many pretended that they were knowledgeable in the field of mental disorders. For some it was merely a step up the political ladder.

Westmont was slowly dying; the staff was abandoning it, and families were full of frustration, stress, resentment and fears. But the families were trying to resuscitate Westmont with their endless efforts of assembly, in meetings with representatives and media. They would not give up until the last breath was drawn.

This Westmont game was likened to a baseball game in the ninth inning, two outs, and two strikes! Would they win this game in the end or lose it? "It's not over till it's over," was a cry heard in one of the family meetings.

The governor received a request from the families that Westmont have an administration drawn from within its realms and personnel from its area. Out-of-towners had already proven their lack of concern for both staff and patients.

Some things are evident and need not be verbally rein-forced. People can sense a false attitude and a lack of motivation and performance, and can perceive self-indulgence of power. The outsiders' air of arrogance and importance permeated their stature, and most would not signify a return of an address such as "Good Morning" from the peon staff.

The governor seemed to be the only hope for the families. He was considered a deeply religious man with moral convictions as to the treatment of human beings.

A new appointee, Pamila Houston, replaced Ethel Richter and was gracious enough to meet with the families. She sounded more compassionate than the rest, and the families believe that, due to her efforts, the statue of St. Dymphna was returned to the chapel, and the families would be able to meet once more on state grounds. Now all that was needed was the reinstatement of Mr. Randall and the confirmation announcement that Westmont was staying open. There were already staff positions to be filled posted, although no new announcement was made. But this certainly was a positive sign. This saga had gone on long enough and now all of the state clowns at the helm were gone–except for one.

The Protect the Patient family support group had at last found a reporter on The Quest who was willing to listen to their side of the story. Carolyn A. wanted to know the real truth about how the families felt and the treatment they had received at the hands of the bureaucrats.

The families wasted no time in voicing their disgust and anger about the past two years of publications directed toward abuse, negligence and mismanagement at Westmont.

At last there was someone to print the truth about the dilemmas of the mentally ill and their families. She did this in a professional, investigative manner and proceeded to publish articles relating to this subject.

This was a learning experience, even to Carolyn, and there were a few things that she didn't realize and brought to the attention of the public, hoping to gain their interest and concern.

The consumer advocates for the mentally ill were disturbed by these articles, believing that they would lead legislators to overlook the potential of community placements and would make involuntary commitments easier. Threats of violence are not sufficient to permit commitment.

A few cases that were presented in her column were:

Ronald M. attacked his parents, slashing his blind father's throat and cutting his mother when she attempted to stop him. When the police arrived, Ronald was standing naked, spattered blood all over his body. One month before this incident, the parents had tried to have him committed because they were frightened of his hostile behavior, bizarre gestures and the memory of a similar attack on his older brother. The petition was denied. Ronald was found not guilty by reason of insanity, and is now residing in a state mental facility.

When Beatrice P. became mentally ill, she lost interest in her appearance and became incontinent. She also became mute and self-isolative, withdrawing into some sort of religious obsession, and was often found roaming the streets improperly clothed. She needed help, but because she wasn't violent, she was always released by the courts when her emergency status subsided.

She remained problematic after eight years, but her family could not obtain a diagnosis because she wasn't violent. They would have to lie to the courts and claim that she was violent in order to have her committed for treatment. They had tried to work through the legal system but it hadn't worked.

Carolyn A. interviewed eighty-three families in the urban area, and about one-sixth had to lie in order to have their relatives committed for treatment.

"The mental health system has taught us to be good liars," complained one mental health official.

Another distraught family was repeatedly refused commitment for their ill son, and depended on the criminal justice system to do what the mental health system refused to do. They were willing to have criminal charges brought against their son if it resulted in obtaining treatment. The only negative result could be an "internment," or jail sentence, depending on the judge's decision.

Parents are driven by love or fear–or sometimes both–in an effort to find treatment for their mentally ill children. While at home, their son deluded, hallucinated and responded to voices, resulting in the destruction of their home; knocking out a whole window and its frame; breaking apart a bookshelf; throwing hammers at family members; knocking down walls; and knocking holes in the upstairs rooms.

He had also smashed the family car while his brother was sitting in it and destroyed all but one window. When the police arrived, he threw a large piece of concrete at their car, striking an officer on his thumb. The parents tried to have him committed that evening for treatment, but were turned away because, "He did not seem to be a danger to others."

The parents then had him arrested, a suggestion of the police officer. He went to prison, stating that he wasn't mentally ill.

Families do not want their relatives convicted! They want them committed!

Another case Carolyn presented in her column concerned J. And M., who were married and raised a family and lived at the same address for almost forty years until they ran away from their own son. The son suffered from Bi-Polar Disorder (manic depression) and was unpredictably violent. He was tall, husky and seriously ill. The parents shrank from his fiery fury, and although they frequently sought assistance from the city's mental health system, they were told by them to kick him out of the house!

Police officers, psychiatrists and mental health professionals encourage families to get protection orders in violent behavior
cases. There's nothing more that can be done under some current
mental health systems. And the number of petitions has increased
in recent years.

In another case, J.R.–whose son was mentally ill and
violent–secured a protection order which was not effective. His son
returned often, banging on the doors, threatening to break the
windows, etc. While at home, his son had broken lamps, hurled the
TV across the room, hit his father on the head with a juice bottle
causing cuts and broke mirrors. After residing thirty years at the
same residence, the father moved out, but the mother remained.
J.R. couldn't sleep, was receiving dialysis weekly and could no
longer endure the stress. He needed peace!

Marie's son was in jail. Why? His only crime was coming
home and violating a protection order! She knew that this seemed
cruel, but it was the only way she could protect her family. Her son
suffered from severe schizophrenia, had stopped taking his medications and had started using street drugs.

His history included robbery, vandalism, threats, overdoses
and a near fatal stabbing of his younger sister. He was responding
to voices that told him to "kill." His behavior became more frightening over the years. He had stabbed his sister with a stiletto knife,
puncturing her lung, then ran off into the streets. The police found
him still clutching the stiletto.

Drug programs refuse to handle psychiatric patients, and
psychiatric programs refuse to treat drug offenders. Yet these two
conditions can be intertwined, with the drugs accelerating the
schizophrenic behaviors and the destruction of the brain cells. This
problem and the solutions to it can go around in circles, with no
beneficial actions or reactions by the system as it is today.

Carolyn also investigated the conditions in the metropolitan
hospitals' psychiatric emergency rooms and found that there was a
shortage of short-term beds available for the community residents
due to the increase of crack addicts and overcrowding conditions,
which made it almost impossible to accept new commitments.

Since the closing of admissions at Westmont, the city's only
long-term care facility, a massive overload of emergency services
was created for the mentally ill. Because of these conditions, the
police had no other alternative but, when turned away by these

Jail
Treatment not Jail!

hospitals, to often place these patients into jail cells for protection from both themselves and others.

Even though this is not professionally legal, there is no other choice. The only other alternative is to release them onto the streets or back to their families, who could not cope with their behaviors and uncontrollability.

Patients who were lucky enough not to be turned away were often found strapped to chairs or gurneys for hours at a time–often days–because there were no beds available. In one case a woman spent sixteen days in the emergency room most of the time spent strapped to a gurney.

Due to the overcrowded conditions, these metropolitan hospitals are forced to restrict or close their services, and the mentally ill are fruitlessly transported from one hospital to another. When all attempts are exhausted, they are sometimes taken to the jails or released to the streets or their families.

Jail is a stop measure, but the police realize that these are people and they belong in a hospital.

One mentally ill man died of heatstroke while being held in a van, awaiting psychiatric examination. The emergency room was closed, and he had waited for about an hour, wearing several layers of clothing in ninety degree heat. This tragedy lead the police to start placing these individuals in jail cells. The involuntary commitments (302's) had increased from five to seven thousand in one year's time. The waiting lists continue to grow for admittance to the psychiatric units of all facilities.

The states have an obligation to care for their citizens, and they continue to try to wiggle out of it. They appear to want the mentally ill to just disappear in the crowds. More attention is given to animal rights, gay rights, civil rights, human rights, student rights, etc., but it appears that the mentally ill and their families have no rights.

In Chester County, Pennsylvania, a judge rejected claims of mental illness in the sentencing of twenty-two-year-old Robert Hughes in the slaying of two defenseless people in a convenience store, and the district attorney called the sentence a "just one." "The facts outweighed the evidence of his mental illness," he stated.

Hughes walked into the restaurant in January, 1988, after purchasing a 38 caliber revolver. When he was refused entrance because the restaurant had not yet opened, he forced his way in, posing as a new maintenance man.

The only people in the restaurant were Charles Hegarty and Jean Reider, who were preparing for the business of the day. Hegarty was forced to lie on the floor while Reider was forced to open the safe, which contained about three hundred dollars.

As another employee was about to enter the place, Hegarty waved him off and, shortly afterward, Hughes put the gun to Hegarty's head and shot him. Reider ran into another room and crouched in a corner, and Hughes put the gun to her face and also shot her.

The employee who was waved off by Hegarty called the police. When they arrived, they found both people dead from their wounds.

Psychological problems had plagued Robert Hughes since adolescence. He was evaluated, and it was determined that he had a personality disorder which sometimes resulted in aggressive behavior. Hughes was convicted of first degree murder and was given the death sentence. Less than a month previously, he had been released from a state mental institution and was not considered a threat to himself or others.

His parents were stunned when this judgment was read and later stated, "My son is mentally ill and has been for a long time. This is a tragedy for all families involved!"

The death penalty will probably be appealed when further medical testimony shows his long history of mental problems, but this incident should never have happened. As in the case of Derrick Smith Bey, innocent people were murdered because of the lack of foresight in determining what future behavioral patterns are possible by some of these released patients.

Again, individuals are diagnosed and grouped by a set of symptoms, but no one can predict the intricacies of the subdued thought processes in our minds. Just as snow flakes are different from each other, so are human beings. No two minds or bodies are identical.

The governor's re-election bid would be coming up the following year, and at the forefront of the race was another political official who opposed the closure of Westmont. She criticized his decision, and stated that he was responsible for the hasty manner of transferring these hard-core mentally ill patients into the communities. She used the three examples of patient drownings, and wondered how this extreme monitoring program could possibly result in these deaths, and what excuses could be offered for the

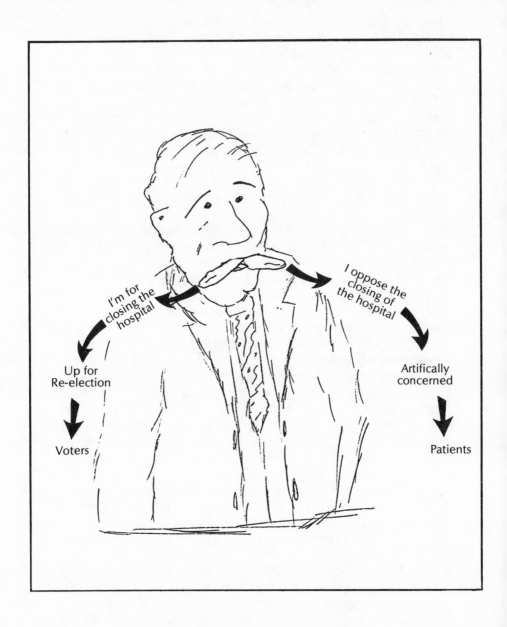

Forked Tongue
State Representative

occurrences.

She had heard and read statements by Knight, Richter and Booker emphasizing how wonderful these placements were, how dedicated the teams of CTT members were and that they knew where every patient was and the progress that they were making. How unrealistic this really was, without enough funds and staff to monitor these hard-core mental patients, who never should have been considered for placement in the first place.

This opposition candidate toured Westmont and saw for herself the conditions within. She appeared pleased with what she found. Several state representatives accompanied her on this unannounced tour, including Mr. K., who had always voiced his opinion for the closure. This man was the representative who had ignored the families who had tried to contact him, and described earlier as speaking out of both sides of his mouth. This female candidate, who wanted to upset the incumbent, stated that the land was "prime real estate" with the state anticipating the sale, and would relieve their responsibilities by placing the patients within the counties.

Mr. K., who had tried to appear concerned while wanting the hospital closed, was now stating that he favored keeping the hospital open. He also agreed with other representatives at this time that he opposed the hospital closing. Yet only the week before, he was concerned, but still wanted the hospital to close.

Lois Booker continued to state the same rhetoric: "The patients were released only after extensive planning. No one, in my opinion, has been put in an unsafe environment." This confirms the asshole decisions and management under her rule described in the events listed in this novel. Did she really believe what she was saying or was she still "snow jobbing" the people? Her incompetency and lies continued, and this was all the more reason to request her removal from the position as Westmont's superintendent.

Her statements to the press sounded like a broken record, playing the same old phrase over and over again, the same as Knight and Richter, as if they had all evolved from the same mold.

It was now almost time for the decision from the governor as to the future of Westmont. this was to prove interesting, with another candidate advocating the reversal of his initial decision to close because a true need existed in this large city for a long term facility unit. We now watched which way the wind would blow. It would soon be forthcoming. The decision could balance and influence the next election.

While this controversy was boiling, Mr. Formbe and the family group would never rest behind the scenes. Their contact with the media, representatives and state officials still insisted that Mr. Randall be re-instated, Booker be removed and the hospital remain open. This never-ending battle was stressing everyone out, but their dedication to the welfare of the mentally ill was unending. Yes! The next few months would tell the story!

Time was descending quickly for the governor's final decision about Westmont. Huddled together behind closed doors, the politicians and administrators, including the governor's secretary, would have to present their comprehensive report.

The staff again would be stressed further, with insinuations that they wouldn't have a position if the hospital closed, and their best bet would be to take their transfers now. Were they talking about the care of the patients? No! All of this added intimidation was introduced before any official announcement was made concerning closing, or remaining open.

This saga was like the story of "The Tiger or the Lady." Would Westmont remain open or would it close? Would the staff have a job or not? Would the families and patients suffer more?

The governor's secretary stated at this meeting that the governor had been misquoted in the press. "He did not say indefinite, he said indeterminate." I guess that the families and the television viewing audience heard it all wrong!

Another meeting was scheduled which would include Lois Booker, Mr. Whitman, and others, the results of which would be gathered in a report for the governor. They were to assess the patients already discharged into the community.

The patients and their families saw that, with these representatives, the deck of cards was already stacked in the state's favor. Hadn't Booker and Whitman and the others tried their best to close the place with all of their planning and scheming and, at every turn, hadn't these plans crumbled around them?

Didn't all of the confrontations and reviews pointing towards all of the oppositions they had encountered cause frustrations and anger? This report which they had to hand to the governor was their last hope of victory. They had already played their hand, and this was the only trump card left.

Mr. K., the state representative, had to see which way the pendulum was swinging. Public outcry for something to be done with these chronically mentally ill patients had finally surfaced! The constituents in his voting block wanted the hospital closed but, as a state representative, he was also obligated to listen to other opinions that wanted the hospital to remain open.

The city planning committee postponed the land reuse meeting because there was an outcry for public hearings concerning the controversy over Westmont.

Because of the drowning incidents and a list of other occurrences involving released patients, the consensus was that the state had underfunded and mismanaged the hospital for many years. The state had wanted to get out of the mental health business, and closing the hospital would have solved their problems. If this plan had worked, all of the mental hospitals could have ben phased out in the same manner. This only proves that their knowledge of schizophrenia was nil. These were not just human beings who were mentally sick, but people who really could not function in a community setting. Many had been out there before and failed in their attempt to exist socially because of lack of supervision and refusal to continue their medication routines. Throughout this novel, it had been emphasized that what was left in Westmont were the hard-core mental patients. There has to be a place for these individuals to exist and be cared for! It is hoped the past experiences of chaos and deaths will finally sway the states around the country to realize that there is a great need for these places, regardless of what the advocates say. The advocates made it out there, but not everyone can do the same!

Here it was, past the due date of closure, and at this point people were exhausted from fighting the system. Yet there were rays of hope from recent statements made by some of the state officials. Things remained in limbo, with the big decision yet to come from the governor. He was carrying a heavy schedule which would lead him in other directions at this time. There was a meeting with the president concerning the country's education system and a bid decision concerning the abortion issue in the state. These topics superseded the issue of the mentally ill at this time, although the governor had declared the first week of October "Mental Health Awareness Week."

Although the families had found an interested reporter on The Quest, Carolyn, there was also an opposing staff reporter. She had gained more interest and public awareness through her recent articles, and she had also become more knowledgeable and con-

Do they beat you?
Do they assault you?
Do they strap you down?
Do they lock you up?

positive questions usually
give positive answers
from mental patients

= They don't beat you do they? – (No)

Reporters from the Quest and T.V. News

cerned as a result of her investigations.

Another reporter for The Quest, again started bashing the hospital and its staff in his column. For every step gained in the right direction to keep the hospital open, the opposition and the consumer advocated had another opportunity to gain the spotlight in the media.

His column stated that he had seen things such as patients lying on the floor, a woman taking out her false teeth while placing a cigarette in her mouth, and another patient wearing shoes three sizes too large. Yet he did not stipulate that these were mental patients who existed in the mental hospital, and were not the norm.

Did he expect them all to use the chairs while sitting? He did not know the patient's backgrounds, and yet felt justified to make these statements in his column. Did he know that some patients refuse to sit on chairs and prefer lying on the floors, although prompted many times during the day, day after day, month after month?

Did he understand that patients will often put on layers of clothing if not stopped and will steal other clothing from peers when the opportunity arises?

He also stated in his column there was a lack of therapeutic activities, and the patients sat in their rooms with their bags packed. This last statement that he made was not at all evident; yet on the other hand, these patients are not stupid because they are mentally ill. They were tense because of all the controversy surrounding the hospital. They were also frustrated about and uncertain of their futures and often would ask questions of the staff about the status of any decision which might have been made that they may have missed.

This reporter still did not blame the state system that had transferred many professionals to other state facilities. He would state that it would only be reasonable for these transfers to occur in lieu of the end of September closing notice.

It was also ironic that this bashing column appeared on the same day the governor arrived in the city. Ethel Richter's statements, along with Mr. Tweedil's opinions, were cited in his column, and were meant to sway the governor's final decision.

The pressures and powers of the press were again a dynamic force used to gain the consensus of the public.

It seemed that for every ally gained by the families and patients, an opposing force would arise, but the real conspiracy here was against the mentally ill!

During "Mental Health Awareness Week," the state social service workers union held a press conference at the gate of Westmont. The purpose of this news conference was to launch a state-wide campaign to prevent further tragedies due to the threatened closing of the hospital.

This was to be a state-wide appeal for the state to keep its mental hospitals open. A funeral wreath was placed on the grass with the names of the three patients who had drowned because of premature discharging displayed.

The state hospitals across the state were under attack by misguided community and patient advocate groups. Although deinstitutionalization was a good idea, the real aim was simply to save money at the patient's expense. As caretakers, they could no longer stand by and silently tolerate the "Big Lie" that stated that you could rob the institutions to pay for community care!

The community mental health systems were already overtaxed and, consequently, people who required hospitalization could not get help. There must be access to beds at all levels of care!

Carolyn A. was present at the press conference as were the three main television news media channels. The gathering of these professionals and family members again upset the administrators of Westmont, who quickly responded by sending the security guards out in force to meet the group which was gathered in front of the main gate of the hospital. They forced the removal of the funeral wreath, stating that it was on state property. This gathering would only have access to the pavement and not on even a small parcel of grass on which the wreath was placed.

At least now the media would witness this expulsion by the state administrators. The automobiles and vans parked on the grounds also had to be removed or else be ticketed as trespassing. Did the administration really believe these petty deeds would halt the efforts of those fighting for the mentally ill patients? This is what it really was, a fight!

Bumper stickers were passed out across the state which read, "State Hospital Closing: Capital Punishment for the Mentally Ill." Yes! The movement of state-wide efforts in this direction had begun! This novel has alleged all along that the state was the real abuser. This consensus was becoming affirmed, state-wide recognition was now swelling and was "on a roll."

One of the social workers related at this meeting that just the previous evening, Mr. Tweedil, a consumer advocate, and two other advocates had permission to take three patients on a shopping trip, but instead, it was learned, they had taken the patients to a fast food chain to be interviewed by a segment of the television media. This was a blatant act of deceit by the advocates who had not received permission to do this. This is another case of proven frustration on the part of the advocates when the consensus leaned toward keeping the hospital open. What would be done now? Would they still be allowed to take patients from the grounds? This incident would be closely watched by the staff. What rights do the advocates have? They already seemed to have access to the patients charts whenever they wished.

With Lois Booker in charge, the families remained very uneasy. Someone then wrote to the governor requesting her removal. She must have been contacted concerning the letter because, soon afterward, she would call upon one of the members of the family support group and arrange a meeting off the grounds.

The conversation between Lois Booker and the family member lasted a good three hours. Booker wanted to know why the staff at the hospital and the families did not like her! She was told that the reason was her lack of compassion, concern and trust towards families and patients. Booker appeared very humble and listened to these allegations with intensity.

Shortly after this quiet meeting, Mr. Formbe called Booker on the telephone, and they talked for at least an hour. Mr. Formbe wanted to know why the consumer advocates had availability to the charts and records of the patients. Who was responsible for their actions, especially the incident of taking three patients to a fast food chain to talk with reporters? The family group was very upset with the authority given these advocates concerning their relatives.

"You are telling the press that Westmont would be rehiring professional treatment team employees," Mr. Formbe stated. "You have a dedicated, professional, experienced social service worker, Mr. Randall, who was fired without good reasons, and you know it. He only wanted what was best for these patients and opposed the closing of the hospital. Why don't you reinstate him? I know all about the litigation coming up and the grievances filed, but you can bring him back!"

Booker did not respond to this statement, but it must have made an impact and aroused her feelings about the growing strength of the families in the support group.

Mr. Randall called a friend at the hospital one evening and stated excitedly, "Guess what? I received a phone call today, and I'm going to be reinstated with back pay and benefits! I will start working in two weeks, but it won't be at Westmont. I will be working at another state hospital." This occurred only a few days after Mr. Formbe had spoken to Booker. Perhaps she realized that there were no grounds for his dismissal in the first place, and the state could not substantiate a reasonable cause for his firing.

It also appeared that Ms. Booker, knowing that the families were a very determined group, desired a better relationship with them, and this action would please the group.

Was she trying to fool the families by displaying some compassion and interest at last? A patient who had grounds once wandered into her office. His entrance and his babbling annoyed her to the point that she called someone to remove him from her office. He was escorted back to his building, and his ground privileges were taken away. Isn't this a form of patient abuse? This should raise a question as to her experience with mental patients. Do you think that she could endure an eight hour day on duty in a ward? This action only displayed Booker's low tolerance level, and that patients really seemed to annoy her. There was no one around at the time to impress, and her true personality was exhibited. These "human beings" are only numbers in her census count, and were only bodies to be counted. She still wasn't to be trusted!

At last, in early October, Mr. K., the state representative, arranged a meeting with the families. This meeting would last an hour and one-half. The families felt free to ventilate both their frustrations and their expectations for their relatives who reside in Westmont.

He appeared interested–as they all do–now that he had turned his thinking process in their direction, and promised that he would consider asking the other representatives to support maintaining Westmont for the chronically mentally ill. The meeting seemed fruitful, and the families wanted him to support them, but who could tell if this was also an act for their benefit.

Were things turning around at last? Could this really be happening as a result of the relentless contracts and meetings with the state officials? We would soon learn the fate of Westmont, and the governor would soon be expected to publicize his decision.

The staff and the patients were still apprehensive about the uncertainty of this decision. The patients had, on many occasions, overheard conversations pertaining to this forthcoming decision.

They also felt anxious and, intermittently, one would ask the staff, "Are we staying open? Do you think we'll close?"

Although chronically ill, these patients are alert, and many are oriented as to time, place and person. Many patients expressed a desire to stay at Westmont, and many patients felt the security of the hospital, with a staff that they had known for many years.

Positive things were happening now, and we were on the upswing. Mr. Randall had been reinstated; the statue of St. Dymphna was returned; the families could meet once more on state grounds; we were opened indefinitely–at least until the governor's decision came down; there were postings for new positions at the hospital. Until this decision was made, everyone felt that we were in a whirlpool and, at this point, no one could predict the outcome!

The middle of October was here, and a decision had not yet been announced by the governor as to the disposition of Westmont. This lead to another opportunity for The Quest to put forth further accusatory statement by ex-patients relating to "hospital abuse," not necessarily in Westmont, but any state institution.

It was true that at this period of stagnation, patients had no activities and would spend their time smoking cigarettes, watching television or walking around the wards or grounds, if they had ground privileges. Westmont had been placed in this position by the state that chose to transfer the experienced, professional, recreational, social personnel to other state hospitals. They also diverted funds from the hospital itself to outside community treatment teams and placements.

Mental illness in this country appears to be the least considered and the most underfunded malady of its citizens. In the media, physical abuse always alluded to staff upon patients, yet the physical abuse inflicted upon the staff and the resulting disabilities are unmentionable.

State hospitals will always be decried in the media, yet until enough funds are released for smaller community facilities or group homes properly staffed and supervised, the institution remains the only alternative for the chronically mentally ill when all insurances and monies are exhausted.

Ethel Richter, who was no longer an official in the placement program, finally admitted to the media that the original team assessments were willing to take risks with some patients, believing that they deserved a chance to live in the community. The second team

141

would exercise more "caution." She stated, "You have a choice of looking at something fairly conservatively or fairly openly.

In most articles bashing the hospital and its staff, no mention was made about the valuable grounds occupied by Westmont. Since the recent suicides of the patients who were already placed in the community this seemed to be a no-no.

On a recent radio talk show, a resident of the near-by community and the leader of its civic association stated, "We never asked to have Westmont closed! We only wanted the forensic unit vacated."

In this current stage of eddy, and with the status of Westmont's future hanging in the balance, Mr. Whitman was now saying, "If Westmont closes..."

In a personal interview on television with Geraldo Rivera, he admitted that he was an ardent advocate to close state hospitals but, seeing the increase of street people and the other events that had happened, he now did not believe that he did the right thing, but at the time it sounded very humane.

On two consecutive days, articles appeared in The Quest after interviews with Knight and Richter. Knight took this opportunity to try to exonerate herself by defending her action in the placement program. She stated "The CTT has worked really well," and gave herself a better than average mark. She made no references to the deaths by drowning, the suicides or other disturbing incidents that had occurred due to these discharges. She also took the opportunity to announce her resignation as the Deputy Secretary of Welfare, and stated that it was a result of all the controversy surrounding Westmont. "No one was homeless, no one was living alone or with family without supervision or monitoring."

These were the words she spoke to The Quest. Why did all of the previously discussed events happen if this was so? Knight continued to say that the initial closing plans had not provided the funds or the adequate staff; in addition, there was the constant bickering between state and city officials over these important issues. She also blamed the state for requesting the discharges to be conducted and orchestrated by outsiders from another state. Both Knight and Richter were brought in from Ohio because they had run similar operations in that state.

The following day, Ethel Richter had her turn with the media and blamed pressures from the governor's office for wanting a hasty closure of Westmont. She stated, "We needed more time and more money, and we also needed a free hand, without interference from the politicians. Political decisions interfered with clinical decisions. It was finally stated that the greatest single mistake was the decision to close the admission unit of Westmont before community programs were in place. "This resulted in psychiatric emergency rooms in the metropolitan hospitals backed-up with the long-term patients and no place for them to go."

Ethel Richter felt free to converse with the media at this time, as she no longer had ties with the state and was employed with the city in their mental health services department. It has been stated all along that these leaders were puppets in the political system, but were silent during the tragic events that happened to patients discharged from Westmont.

Even if they had felt that these quickie discharges were wrong, they had not allowed their consciences to motivate them into doing the right thing. Their inactions were at the expense of human life.

The halting of discharges was still in effect while the governor's decision was awaited. In the meantime, Booker was maintaining a three story building which would house nineteen discharged patients who had previously been scheduled to leave. In order to maintain these beds during the interim, $850.00 per patient per month was being paid by the taxpayers to hold these bed spaces. The taxpayers' money was again being wasted at a hefty sum of $16,250.00 per month just for holding these beds until the time when these discharges would take place. Suppose this never happened ! What an expense and waste of money!

With Knight and Richter gone from Westmont's placement programs, Booker stood alone as the remaining person from this three ring circus. Feeling somewhat shaky, but afraid to exhibit her feelings of rejection by both staff and families, she would soon arrange a meeting with these families, which would also include Mr. Randall.

A shocking statistic which the public is not aware of is that mental illness is the number one disease in the country, and yet there are never enough monies allocated by the government for its research.

There are more hospital beds in this country occupied by psychiatric illnesses than any other of the leading diseases. This figure can be computed by including state mental hospitals, private psychiatric hospitals and psychiatric wings in general metropolitan facilities. Not all patients are treated directly in hospitals, and various cities and counties have numerous out-patient treatment centers that can help to stabilize the illness. Many schizophrenics can function quite well in society provided they continue their medication and group therapies as prescribed. There are countless people who refuse treatment or admit that they have a problem. You can certainly recall crossing someone in your lifetime that you thought was weird!

Once diagnosed as schizophrenic, one-third of those diagnosed can have complete remission after the first crisis. Two-thirds will need further treatment, and the many may become terminally ill and need continued hospitalization. These shocking facts are not generally known to the public. With the drug problems of today, we can look forward to an alarming increase of mental illness in the future.

Large public institutions are being depopulated strictly as a way of saving money, not for the purpose of life improvement for these patients in the outside world. This massive shift of the mentally ill to outside facilities such as boarding homes and half-way houses is still underfunded and understaffed, resulting in the gigantic increase in the population of street people in America. Public outcry is only directed toward their own safety and the conditions which they may be forced to face. It is only because the mentally ill street people have become problematic, by urinating and defecating in the streets, lying in peoples' paths when walking, and, at times, being overbearing or assaultive to other citizens, that people will address the issue.

Years of warehousing patients in state institutions was followed by years of dumping patients into many low standard boarding homes or outside care centers, which eventually lead the patients to the streets. Many of these patients eloped because of poor treatment; many simply wandered away and could not find their way back.

As stated earlier, foundations have been formed for animal rights, heart disease, diabetes and cancer, yet not one special organization has been submitted to the public to fight mental illness. It is only recently that there is even mention of depression and other mental disorders, but this is presented mostly one-sidedly and all of the facts are not investigated before presentation.

All of the so-called experts profess to know all about schizophrenics and the effects of medications upon them. A guest on a television panel stated that the medications produced violent, reactive behaviors and therefore should not be used! A woman in the audience said, "What would be happening in the community if no one took medications? Would there then not be more chaos and crimes? This could naturally not be given a direct answer, as no one knows!

Why is diabetes not controlled by medication in all diabetics? Why is hypertension not controlled by medication in all hypertensives? What works for some does not work for all!

The public seems ready to sue the psychiatrist when destructive incidents occur in society. The complexities of the mind are never completely unfolded. We are only guessing at this point, and comparison of one individual to another can still not predict an oncoming behavioral pattern. In many cases, a leopard does not change his spots, but can be momentarily subdued.

As in all diseases, trial and error, experimentation and comparison may lead to the road to recovery, but mental disorders are still in an experimental stage, as no one can predict the feelings and emotional tolerance of the mind!

What precipitates schizophrenia? Is it a chemical imbalance? Is it environmental? Is it heredity? These have all been targeted in studies, but the real cause is yet to be unmasked!

In comparison to other maladies, it appears that a minute portion of governmental funds are directed toward research or treatment of mental disorders in this country, yet it is the number one disease. This disease can tear families as well as communities apart. This disease can lead to crimes, increase in jail populations, street people, even deaths. This disease is still misunderstood by professionals, judges and the public. If you or your family are not affected with mental disorders, you can thank God for it, but you should also learn compassion and tolerance toward the afflicted.

State institutions were "snake pits" years ago, but the treatment and care of the mentally ill has come a long way! When news reporters interview ex-mental patients, their interpretations of treatment can appear shocking. The ex-patients have spoken of being thrown into seclusion without food and water for days, and that they were made to sleep in their own excrement, but this was not seen to be happening by the staff and nursing personnel and, in this day and age, would not be tolerated by the nursing staff.

You have yet to hear of a discharged patient praising their

treatment because many lack insight into their illness. The media is always quick to seek a piece of sensationalism without investigation into the backgrounds of these patients and their families.

There is a constant fight for government recognition of the issue of mental illness.

Today there is an influx of popularity of horror films. Children of twelve or thirteen years old are having "gross out" parties at home, and are renting violent movies. Some of these films are too violent to be shown on the big screen, and many of these films are specially made for home videos.

Suspense and gore is enjoyed by most teenagers today, but on several occasions in various parts of the county, these gorey crimes were carried out as they were portrayed on the screen. Children today seem more callous and less sensitive. Their fantasy violence is different from reality, yet everyday in the news media there are reports of rape and murders.

Television has changed the way we live, and the children of today are exposed to violence and nudity. The producers of these films state that the children are aware of what is real and what is not. Parents feel that these films are a threat to this younger generation, and they are abrasive and dangerous to the growth and molding of their personalities.

It is true that every child was exposed to some form of violence in films, cartoons and comic books, but the exposure was never as explicit and gorey as today's films.

Imagine renting one of these films and showing it to an unstable, mental person who may be living in the community. Do you think they would know the difference between fantasy and reality? Why are some of the behaviors in these films imitated in crimes by "normal" people?

If children can become callous and insensitive, don't you think that these films could influence a twisted mind with tragic results?

Many patients who suffer from auditory or visual hallucinations, have stated that the TV was talking to them or about them. To them these voices become reality, and constant exposure to violence may be responsible for precipitating true violence.

In the latter days of October, 1989, television talk show host Larry King interviewed Janice Swann, a "peeping tom" victim who was shot in the head while sitting in her living room peeling potatoes. She felt as it she had been electrocuted and didn't realize she had been shot. As she struggled to get up, she fell down in the hallway and discovered that she had lost her sight and her hearing. Janice underwent ten hours of surgery in a Washington, D.C. hospital and remained in intensive care for almost two weeks. This episode left Janice with loss of feeling in the left side of her head, but, fortunately, she regained her sight and hearing, and she can also react normally in a given situation.

Mr. King asked, "Why did he shoot you? Why were you shot?" Janice replied, "I don't know! I never met [the assailant] until the trial. Brogsdale, the shooter, had been recently released form an institution and, shortly after, was reported to have exposed himself near a local college but was never picked up by the police.

At the time of the interview with King, Janice was in the process of suing the psychiatrist who had released this man into society. Her lawyer, John Coale, stated, "During the trial, the psychiatrist stated that it was okay for Brogsdale to be free. This peeping tom shot and killed five people and wounded six others. This all took place in a ten week period, and he was masturbating while the shootings were taking place."

Brogsdale's psychiatrist, Dr. Peter Roma, stated at the trial that, "He was under my care, and we all will be safe."

The reason for the lawsuit was to collect damages for the victim, and to expose the irresponsibility of the decision to place the patient into society by the psychiatrist, and his decision to treat his patient in the outside community setting.

It was said on the show that psychiatrists cannot predict danger and should not be sued, as they are not responsible for all of the bad acts that happen in society.

Dr. Paul Fink, president of the American Psychiatric Association, said that twenty million dollars will be spent in the treatment of mental patients. There is only fifteen dollars spent in research per schizophrenic patient, but that one hundred fifty dollars is spent for research per cancer patient. Twenty years ago we knew nothing about cancer, but now it is being treated and cured.

Unless more monies are directed toward research for mental disorders, we cannot hope to be as successful. Funds for mental institutions have been cut in this country, and there are insufficient alternative treatment centers to supervise and direct these ex-patients in the community.

Violent behaviors generally are not predictable and can only be monitored by the patient's willingness to get treatment. Psychiatrists are asked by lawyers to testify as expert witnesses on behalf of their clients, but very often psychiatrists must answer "yes" or "no" and cannot relate specific answers as to future violent behaviors. The judge makes the decision!

Dr. Fink stated, "Crime is not one of our illnesses, and few criminals are mentally ill! This suit is a tragic situation, but psychiatrists should not be sued. They are not responsible for what happens later in society."

A caller to the King show from Oregon said that, since the courts rely on the testimony of psychiatrists, they should not testify if they cannot predict violence. Why can't you sue the parole board? You can't sue the parole board because they are immune, and it is against the law to attempt to sue them.

A caller from San Francisco stated that her son was threatened with a knife by a street person, but no criminal charge was brought against this person. This street person had a ten year history of psychiatric treatment, including medications and electric shock therapy. All the judge said was that he needed more counseling by a therapist. The panelists both stated that he should have been placed in jail!

Dr. Fink stated that one-third of our homeless are mentally ill. There are six million homeless, and two million of them are mentally ill. This is a result of the deinstitutionalization process that started in the early seventies.

A caller from Tennessee stated that his sister was stabbed and killed by her ex-husband, who had been released from the psychiatric hospital on a holiday. Only the week before when he was allowed out, he had held his son at gunpoint.

When questioned by the panel, "Did you ask why the psychiatrist released him?" the answer was, "No. It's in court now."

Mistakes are made. Psychiatry is not a perfect profession! Thirty-six thousand psychiatrists are handling millions of people. Mass murderers are mostly under psychiatric care and on psychiatric medications. There are usually ten or twelve mass murders in a decade.; But this is so minimal, and only a small percentage of patients are this violent.

Mr. Coale was asked if a patient is released on a technicality, where is the attorney's responsibility? The decision rests on who is more clever and capable.

The people want the laws to change to make the psychiatrists more responsible. This should also apply to the judges and lawyers!

The first week of November, 1989, had passed and no decision had been announced. The governor had been too busy with other problems throughout the state the past two months, and it appeared that mental illness would again be place on the back burner. It was reported that relevant papers were on his desk and remained untouched.

Other problems that superseded Westmont were women's rights, the abortion issue, prison riots occurring in various parts of the state, fires and massive destruction of property, and support for upcoming political candidates who were up for election throughout the state.

The mayor of the city maintained his silence concerning city problems relating to mental health and street people.

The families could not remain silent any longer, and while awaiting the decision, their patience was becoming short. They were granted time on a local radio talk show to appeal to the public that there was a need for a psychiatric hospital in their area.

Mr. Formbe and Mr. Donatti, as well as other family members, were guests. The host, Richard Hayes, was very gracious and allowed the families time to express their plight and reply to the call-in audience. The following is a paraphrase of the broadcast:

Host: "Are the families satisfied the way that the hospital is being operated?"

Formbe: "The governor must decree that this city needs this hospital! We're dumping the patients everywhere!"

Host: Explain this wonderful "Plan" of the state's.

Mitchell: "Neighbors want the hospital closed, but that old cliche "not in my neighborhood" is still decried."

Host: "Why is the hospital a better setting?"

Mitchell: "More things are available there. The doctors are on hand for emergencies. There are teams assigned to a certain number of patients in the community, and when [these teams] call in sick or take a vacation, there are no replacements. Another thing! The hospital has quiet rooms in which to calm down agitated patients, but these homes don't have the advantage to keep altercations from happening between patients."

Host: "Mitchell, what's your interest here?"

Mitchell: "My brother has been there for eighteen years, and I know something about it. He'd probably be dead if the hospital closed."

Host: "Can you care for him at home?"

Mitchell: "No! It's too much of an emotional drain on the family and the patient. There are too many pressures, and I can't do the right thing by him. If there's no money, I can't care for him. This is a vicious circle, and, for some families, it could be dangerous. Society takes advantage [of these people] when they are on the street, by robbing them, beating them and sexually assaulting them."

Donatti: "My daughter has been hospitalized there for ten years. We can't cope at home. She won't shower and gives us a hard time. She had turned on loved ones and they want to move out. They can break up homes and families."

Host: "How do you reach the decision to put away your relatives?"

Donatti: "As I explained before, we can't cope and it is a financial burden. The doctor helps to commit them. They find the place. Private hospitals don't want suicidal patients. I know of one case where a patient was restrained for twenty eight days, and the bill came to $28,000.

Formbe: "Where is the mayor? He didn't try to fight for this hospital, and yet this is his city? We want readmission started. The state rents houses with tremendous amounts of monies spent for rents."

Host: "You folks live this nightmare seven days a week. How can outsiders know what you have to go through?"

Donatti: "Most patients receive social security checks monthly, which go directly to the state and help to pay for their care. They are paying some of their way. Where does the thirty-nine million dollars go which they say they are receiving a year to provide care to these patients?"

Host: "We'll go to the telephones now."

Catherine: "Fifteen years ago, my mother was abused there."

Formbe: "It's not that way today, madam."

G.L.: "How can we empty so many places? Where do they put the people if these hospitals close: The homeless and these boarding homes must be monitored more carefully than they are now!"

Donatti: "Hospitals are different today than they were years ago. They provide a wholesome, safe environment.

Host: "These families here live day by day with their frustrations and fears because they have loved ones there. They are frequent visitors there and would know if something was wrong."

Marie: "I'm all for keeping the hospital open. I'm a guardian for a patient, and I do legal work. The people that say 'abuse' do not live with people like this. Would you hold back a patient, or would you let them bite you? If you grab him, and he receives a bloody nose or black eye, are you an abuser? I give credit to the people who are working there. This girl that I care for breaks out windows all the time, and the neighbors are scared."

Formbe: "I never heard of anyone there who had been prosecuted for abuse. Of course abuse is criminal!"

Donatti: "Problems are corrected on the spot, but in the case of abuse, would you close the whole hospital because of it?"

Host: "Your families have seen part of the operations of that hospital, and your loved ones seem to be treated properly by the staff, so, therefore, you would know."

Donatti: "I've seen the doctors and nurses go the extra mile, and I see dedication and concern. If you close the hospital, you will have dead people on the streets."

Host: "There's still a stigma attached to mental illness, and is it better to put them in a back room somewhere and forget them?"

Formbe: "I want to tell the listeners to come on grounds, and come to mass on Sunday and sing with the patients. I do every week. We have a wonderful chapel."

Host: "Did you say that land developers want the land?"

Formbe: "We want three buildings, which is less than one-fifth of the land."

Host: "How much do the developers want?"

Formbe: "They want it all! They don't care what they are doing to the patients. You should have seen how disappointed they were when the governor stopped the discharges indefinitely."

Donatti: "There are no more developmental areas in the city, and somebody said, 'Let's get this piece of land.' "

Host: "I heard that a family deeded this parcel of land solely for the benefit of the mentally ill. Where is this legal document?"

Formbe: "If anyone listening knows, or is related to this family and knows where the papers are, please call the information to us!"

Charles: "Tell me about the advocates! They are professing self-help to replace psychiatry. Smith and Tweedil continue to state 'abuse, filth, etc,' but they really have private interests and motives. Smith insisted that the hospital was as bad as it was forty years ago, and was thrown off of the last talk show by the host for being unruly, agitated and loud."

Host: "The callers, for the most part, are relating to fifteen or twenty years past."

Donatti: "Smith and Tweedil would benefit financially if they had their way!"

Host: "Thank you, gentlemen, for putting the spotlight on this subject, what is needed and what has to be done."

Formbe: "Anyone can join our organization, Protect the Patients family support group, and get involved. Please get on our side and give us a chance. The hospital can become the best there is!"

Donatti: "Protect the Patients means protect!"

Mitchell: "Report abuse if you see it. Be aware, but give credit where credit is due."

Donatti: "The deaths by drowning and the suicides] but if the remaining patients are at the bottom of the barrel and the least competent, they will be killed, murdered or commit suicide. What about people ten years from now? Where will they go? We are speaking for all of the families of the future. Westmont is the answer. It is the last stop! All of these patients have been through half-way and boarding houses, but couldn't make it out there!"

Even as the show concluded, the stigma was still there, for these families continued to use alias names for fear of recognition. Perhaps with an audience of fifty three million, their message would gain the attention, and we are sure that some listeners out there have personally related to their plight.

There were an equal number of positive and negative callers who remarked about Westmont, but the majority of the negative remarks related to the past. Treatment today for mental patients is more humane, but a cure is yet to be found.

Throughout the United States, thousands of incidents in the communities are not publicized in the news media, and only by scanning the newspapers can one find short articles, on a middle or back page, relating to some atrocity committed by a mentally deranged individual. Once printed there is usually hardly any follow-up articles to relay the outcome of these criminal mental incidents.

The news media has not changed for two hundred years concerning information about catastrophic occurrences causing the deaths of innocent people. By not addressing the issue of this serious illness that affects millions of people, the "hush-hush" tactics have further stigmatized families.

In November, 1989, for instance, a small article relating a horror tale of a real tragedy appeared on page twenty of an urban newspaper. In Louisburg, North Carolina, a twenty-year-old young mother, K. McK., sadistically butchered her three children, ages one, two and two months. She had mutilated their bodies as if cutting a piece of meat. Using a steak knife, she stabbed each child at least one hundred times, cutting open their abdomens and removing their organs. These organs were found strewn about a bedroom.

She then tied together the remains with a cord, and dumped them on a neighbor's doorstep. K. McK. was taken into custody after she burst into a neighbor's house naked, incoherent, covered with blood and displaying visible superficial, self-inflicted stab wounds. She was committed to a state mental hospital for psychiatric observation.

If no state mental hospital were in existence, where would she have been placed? The advocates and libertarians believe that mental patients can all function in a community setting. "Do away with these warehouses," they say.

What alternative is suggested for these violent, erratic hard-core patients? This woman had evidently been suffering from mental illness and perhaps had never received treatment. Schizophrenics sometimes do not seek help, nor do they believe that they are ill. Are there enough mental health centers in the communities for these individuals to receive the help they need? And when in a crisis, would they have enough sense to seek help?

There is an urgent need for the government to allocate more funds for research programs for mental illness. The families of these patients are gaining strength in their support groups and can have a definite impact by consistently, persistently contacting their representatives and demanding research and better treatment for the mentally ill.

Governmental monies are doled out for unimportant, insignificant, useless studies which the tax payers are not even aware of. There is funding for silly things such as studies of the sexual habits of frogs, or monies spent toward "art," such as a crucifix in a jar of urine, at a price of more than fifteen thousand dollars.

The movement of patients from hospital to neighborhood health care centers was really a policy of eviction, preceded by the exposure of these hospitals' horrors, dating back to the forties, with the comparisons to today's treatment of the mentally ill. These movements were preceded by a crusading libertarian sector of journalists, seeking sensationalism through sadistic exposure.

An added incentive to empty institution beds was federal funding by Medicare and Medicaid programs, which only paid partial costs in the metropolitan hospitals. The sad story behind the deinstitutionalization for many was insufficient and underfunded community mental health programs or centers to provide continued care and treatment once discharged.

Most mentally ill persons can live normal lives in the community, providing they continue outpatient care. Under the Kennedy administration, the shifting of mental patients from dungeon-like settings to these mental health centers began. Instead of finding facilities to accommodate these patients once discharged, thousands ended up on the streets, where they were regarded as nuisances or threats to society, while others ended up in the jails.

Psychiatrist E. Fuller Torrey stated that this portrayed program was a "social reform turned to disaster." Funding cutbacks disabled the program. After being proposed in the seventies, this National Plan was already dead on arrival on Capitol Hill, and has never fully arisen from the initial groundwork. There is nothing wrong with the proposed plan, but, or course, these programs must be funded sufficiently and staffed as well.

In 1963, the Community Mental Health Centers Act called for the opening of two thousand community centers. Fewer than half came into existence, and, as usual, the bulk of federal funds designated for this purpose was dispersed for other programs such as prevention and therapy for divorced mothers from low income families, and were not spent for the chronically mentally ill.

Bureaucrats continued to dip into special funding for purposes unrelated to their specified purposes. Look at social security as it is today and what it was intended for. Double-dipping, or robbing Peter to save Paul, seems to be the way of governmental bureaucracies that cannot be held accountable for expenditures from these funds. And tax payers are kept ignorant of the use of these funds for these other purposes. You will hear people say that there is fear of security if the monies from the social security funds are spent in other programs, and yet they have paid for this security with their weekly payroll deductions for many years.

Money does not insure good treatment or cure in mental illness. When insurances are exhausted, many times parents or families will obtain second mortgages on their homes to pay for further care of their mentally ill relatives. Over many years, tormented, guilt-filled families funnel their loved ones through a labyrinth of mental health services, only to feel distraught when no obvious benefits or improvements are noted.

There remains a constant shortage of hospital beds and no long-term care community services to keep these patients out of hospitals. The outpatient centers do not have the follow-up programs or personnel needed to insure that patients come for their treatment.

The limited model programs only reach a fraction of those in need of treatment.

A coalition of families are today forcing changes. "The involvement of the families is one of the most important things to happen in the treatment of mental health," said Dr. Hubert Pardes, president-elect of the Psychiatric Association and former director of NIMH (National Institute of Mental Health).

Mr. Formbe stated that the family lawyers stated that they would not have given them two cents for their case against the state two years ago. Because of their persistence, resistance and dedication to the welfare of their families and the mentally ill in general, they have gained recognition by the authorities, and the strength of their convictions can no longer be ignored.

Three months had lapsed since the initial decision to halt discharges indefinitely, and the families and staff still waited. Maybe the decision would not be what was expected, and maybe it would be more than we bargained for, and yet the land use committee continued to hold meetings about the disposition of the land.

Everyone was asking any staff member, "Have you heard anything yet?" For the first time, no one was speculating as to the outcome. The Quest had also been quiet, with only intermittent articles with irrelevant contents and nothing concrete in either direction.

The subject of mental illness was circulating more frequently in the television media, and references to the problematic conditions were increasing. The plight of the burdened families and their frustrations with the mental health system throughout the country leaned more toward the condemnation of the commitment laws and the negative legal judgments being made.

Regardless of any forthcoming decision, the political element of this country must take a more responsive, responsible role in caring for our mentally ill.

If "warehousing" is not the answer, then suitable community placements which are sufficiently funded and staffed would not be a disastrous alternative.

Mental illness will not go away, and society must not continue to turn its back or close its eyes, for this is a real illness. Why must people be personally affected before they feel any concern or compassion toward other human beings?

It is the consensus of the staff and families that the delay of the decision regarding Westmont was partially due to other pressing issues throughout the state. The real important issues were pro-choice (the abortion issue), prison riots, automobile insurance and a new sports stadium, and the mentally ill would again be pushed back into oblivion.

Westmont would hang in limbo with an indecisive future for many months–perhaps even years. The land developers were again meeting in November to divide the property, with parcels of land designated for various enterprises. Even without a decision, they continued to plan for future developments. Did they know more than the staff, families or the present administration, or was the present administration aware of the outcome and not telling the staff?

Two state representatives presided on the Land Use Committee, and it was evident that the politicians certainly had some knowledge about the future of Westmont! It would only be a matter of time–but how long?

Deinstitutionalization will continue to proceed, displacing the mentally ill not only in one state but in all of the states. Unless federal rules are set forth to protect the hard-core, chronically ill, this process will continue, pushing the mentally ill out into the streets, with more of them unable to cope.

Corporations and land developers seem merciless in their endeavors to ignore the wilderness, environment, and displacement of people in order to gain further profits. Bureaucrats favor them if only for possibly improving revenues or tax bases gained by these developments.

Non-productive human beings who are ill are somehow a burden to the urban, suburban and rural counties where dollar signs are more important. A greedy society is less tolerant!

Families today still feel stigmatized and wish to hide their identities from public view. As in the dark ages, they don't want anyone to know that their son, daughter or mother is a victim of mental illness. One father, whose son is considered hard-core, is still fighting to keep Westmont open under an assumed name. There is no other place for his son to go! He can never return home due to the behavioral patterns and volatile personalities that he has assumed. There is no better place for his son than at Westmont, protected from both society and himself.

Many families assume different names when interviewed by radio or television hosts, if only to protect other family members, such as the brothers and sisters who are still in school. Imagine if their classmates knew that their sister or brother were "crazy." What kind of an existence would they have in school? It is well known that children can be very cruel! This can also be said for an ignorant public.

Knowing these facts while producing programs for the public to view, it is hoped that future programs will also include some of the family members, who could participate in these programs incognito. This could be very stimulating and informative for society, as they will have to deal more and more with the mentally ill as they infiltrate their communities while being deinstitutionalized. The public may want to know more then, when it may possibly be too late for some!

The public was fearful of the first telephone because they could not understand how a voice could come out of a wire. Many elders would not place them in their homes. Today there are complex computers that puzzle many people, and yet, with some knowledge and experience, they would not be without one.

The public is also afraid of the mentally ill and do not care to address the issue. Images of "crazy people" are mostly presented through the television or film industry, and they are mostly portrayed in a violent manner. The mentally ill are not all violent or destructive. But many do have inappropriate behaviors and could not function outside of a structured environment.

Many lack survival skills, and many could be taken advantage of by others. There are many patients who have grounds and wander around during the day or go to the corner store. Others go home on day passes or for the weekend or holidays.

These patients are not locked up, as the newspapers say they are, and do not spend their lives in a cage. Many patients are here because they were suicidal, and at any opportunity might injure or even kill themselves. Others are fascinated with starting fires and would be a danger to others or themselves. Some clients acted out sexually, and would masturbate in public or sexually abuse someone if discharged from the hospital.

The patients here are safe from society and self-injury, and they receive all of the necessities of life. There is a great need to maintain an institutional setting. Many of these patients will say that they love it here, that this is their home and they feel safe from intimidation here. Some of these patients can never go home again!

Should we care enough to want to maintain this measure of security for patients afflicted with mental disorders? Or should we just keep our backs turned while the courts are committing them to the streets?

You decide! Are they less than human?

EPILOGUE

In January, 1990, there was an eerie, almost obscene silence regarding the future of Westmont. The media also abstained from any mention of a decision which was to have been made by now from the governor.

The pathetic condition of Westmont's environment displayed the lack of housekeeping, maintenance or attractive dinner trays for patients. The food at times looked as if it had been scraped form the bottom after other had eaten. Everyone remarked that the food was terrible. Maybe it was nourishing, but it certainly looked bad. If we would serve this to our families, we wouldn't be surprised if they would end up throwing it as us. But it was only for the poor mental patients, some of whom would not realize any difference.

There was no activity personnel, and the staff continued to be deleted and replaced by temporary, inexperienced people. This caused alarm and fears of below minimum numbers of staff. This created a dangerous and potentially hazardous situation. The nursing staff was now using physician's order sheets from another state facility, and everyone wondered why Westmont wasn't having any more printed up.

Patients who were sent to outside reassessment centers were now being brought back, and these were patients who could not be placed into the community. Other patients were inconspicuously being transferred out, and, with the returned patients from assessment centers, no one could see too much difference in the census count.

Lois Booker had suddenly decided to retire, and a dinner was held in her honor to celebrate her retirement. Did she know something? Of course! She must have!

Empty beds were being removed from the wards, and one could only guess that they were being moved to another state facility. Still no word was given to staff or patients, but it was plain for everyone to see that something negative was about to happen.

February had arrived, and Mrs. Applegate was home one evening when she received a call from Mrs. Trulock, a registered nurse on duty. She disclosed that all staff members received memos that night from Mr. Whitman, stating that Westmont would soon be closed, either by June or earlier. The memo also stated that all employees would be placed, and their commitments would be honored for their position elsewhere in the state. Mr. Whitman had told a talk radio station in January that he would make a decision tomorrow. Tomorrow never came! Anxious families and staff members waited, and the suspense was a little overwhelming for some. It seems that Mr. Whitman did not have the guts to call a staff meeting to make his announcement, but had instead sent pieces of paper with the information in order to not face the staff and answer any questions.

Equally spineless was the disclosure of Westmont's fate: it was placed in a state budget report and was quietly slipped in a small paragraph on a page midway in the budget document. This was despite the continued debates over the hospital's future.

More important than the mentally ill, who do not vote nor pay taxes, were monies appropriated towards prisons, police, economic development, education and human service (geared mostly toward women), and the lowest percent towards "other."

The governor was coming up for re-election this year, and it was the consensus of many that the land developers, who had supposedly backed him in the last election, did not have "their land" and would probably take back their financial support unless this land was delivered into their hands!

The new deputy state official, who replaced Mary Knight, visited the hospital for several days, warning staff of an early closure. One nurse asked her, "What if the families get another injunction to keep the patients from departing for another state facility on short notice?"

She replied, "We're not worried about that. We have our own

160

lawyers!

"Where will you go when we close?" she added.

"Oh, I'm going to retire," said the nurse, who was now sixty-four years old.

The deputy then stated, "You better get your papers in order fast!"

Mr. Tramp, an LPN, was also asked his intentions, to which he replied, "I can't stand the politics here!"

"What do you mean," she said, "Democrat or Republican?"

"No, I mean the internal politics here at the hospital."

The deputy turned to another official who accompanied her to the wards, and was overheard to say, "The train has already left the station."

Did this mean that because of his remarks that he would not have a placement job? The way that it was said, you could bank on it!

It was then learned that Mr. Silver, a lawyer previously representing the families and the patients, was now working for the state! How much did they pay him? We will never know! It was also suspected that Mr. Silver had some invested interest in the valuable tract of land upon which Westmont Hospital stood.

A patient named Joey, who could not be placed anywhere because of his animalistic, erratic and bizarre behavior, would be placed into a house bought specifically for him by the state, which would be staffed around the clock. The tax payers would never know how governmental agencies were wasting their money.

Westmont was dying and soon would be dead! The bulldozers were waiting over the hill, and, in years to come, future generations would never know what had existed on that land for eighty years. A family who had mental illness in their midst had donated this land for the mentally ill, and had stated that it was never to be sold as long as there was a mental patient occupying it. No one can find documents that specifically stated the conditions, and isn't it ironic that they were not found in the deeds or historical records of the city? What happened to them?

It is often stated that organized crime usually only hurts their own people, where governmental agencies can easily hurt innocent people who happen to be ill! Again I say, "Money talks and bullshit walks."

This ends the saga of Westmont. It will be very interesting to see what really develops on the land where Westmont stood!

REFERENCES

Acker, Carolyn, "Patients at Risk," The Philadelphia Inquirer,
July 17, 1989.

Acker, Carolyn, "Hospital Crowdings Send Patients to Jail," The
Philadelphia Inquirer, September 24, 1989.

Acker, Carolyn, "Defending Her Record," The Philadelphia
Inquirer, October 20, 1989.

Acker, Carolyn and Fine, Mary Jane, "Families Under Siege—A
Mental Health Crisis (Series)," The Philadelphia Inquirer,
September 11-15, 1989.

Bittan, Dave, "Devil's Imps Made Him Push Woman," The Philadelphia Daily News, September 12, 1989.

Dain, Norman, Disordered Minds, Williamsburg: Colonial
Williamsburg Foundation, 1971.

Koltes, Dr. John A., "Au Revoir," Philadelphia Magazine,
Volume 85, (January 1989).

Macloy, Kathleen, "Voices Kill the Prez, and Kids," The Philadelphia Daily News, August 13,1989.

Towarnicky, Carol, "When Mental Illness Strikes," The Philadelphia
Daily News, October 18, 1989.

Wilner, Daniel M. and Walkley, Rosabelle Price and O'Neill,
Edward J., Introduction to Public Health: Seventh Edition
New York: Macmillan Publishing Co., 1978.